GW00570000

Three Tiffies and a Sweeper

Three Tiffies and a Sweeper

by

Eur.Ing. Alfred E. Deeble
C.Eng., FIMarE, FRINA, PE.

The Pentland Press Limited
Edinburgh • Cambridge • Durham • USA

First published in 1997 by
The Pentland Press Ltd.
1 Hutton Close
South Church
Bishop Auckland
Durham

British Library Cataloguing in Publication Data.
A Catalogue record for this book is available
from the British Library.

ISBN 1 85821 520 X

Typeset by CBS, Felixstowe, Suffolk
Printed and bound by Bookcraft Ltd, Bath

DEDICATION

This book is dedicated to Sandra, my wife,
a fine lady with an indomitable spirit.
Patricia Anne, Suzanne May, Caroline Jane, Pamela Jill,
and Deborah Ruth, my pride and joy and daughters.
My ten grandchildren.
Dr David Deeble, a brilliant scientist; Peter Deeble, British and
English amateur golf champion, my nephews.
All those who lived, fought, and died below the waterline;
and members of the Algerines Association.

Ex Chief ERA Alf Deeble
Royal Navy

The Royal Naval Engine Room Artificers badge (shown on the front cover), subscript, Tubal Cain, originates from Genesis 4:22.
'And Zillah, she also bare Tubal Cain,
an instructor of every artificer in brass
and iron: and the sister of Tubal Cain was Naamah.'

CONTENTS

		Dedication	v
		Reference to Royal Naval Engine Room Artificers badge	vi
		Poem by Rudyard Kipling	ix
		Photograph of Three Tiffies and the Sweeper	x
		Acknowledgements	xi
		Foreword	xiii
Chapter	1	Two Tiffies and a Cruiser	1
	2	What is a Tiffy?	4
	3	Up the Line	8
	4	The Three Meet	12
	5	Humanity, Navy Style	14
	6	The Mystery of Draft ALG/C1	19
	7	Westward Ho!	24
	8	Oh! Canada by Train	30
	9	Journey's End	34
	10	Mystery of ALG/C1, Solved	37
	11	Building a Minesweeper	39
	12	Money Problems	42
	13	Half a Day for King George, Half a Day for King Self	46
	14	George Lives It Up	49
	15	Our American Cousins	51
	16	The Sweeper	68
	17	Bye Bye, Toronto	72
	18	'Shooting' the Rapids	75

19 To Salt Water and the Sea   79
20 Engine Trouble   82
21 Repairs in Halifax   84
22 Back to the War   90
23 Two for Leave   94
24 Working-Up   98
25 One Tiffy Down   104
26 To Gib and the Med   106
27 Operation 'Dragoon'   110
28 Malta, Two Tiffies Down   114
29 Sweeping the Approaches to Piraeus   119
30 Operation 'Manna'   121
31 Ted Meets Spiros   124
32 Patching Up The Sweeper   128
33 The Political Scene Ashore   130
34 Civil War   135
35 Churchill Arrives   140
36 The Third Tiffy and Sweeper Part   143

That's Mr Hinchcliffe,' said Pyecroft. 'He's what is called a first-class engine room artificer. If you 'and 'im a drum of oil and leave 'im alone, he can coax a stolen bicycle to do typewritin'.'

from 'Their Lawful Occasions' by Rudyard Kipling.

Dawn off the foreland, the young flood making
Jumbled and short and steep
Black in the hollows and bright where it's breaking
Awkward water to sweep.
'Mines reported in the fairway,
'Warn all traffic and detain.
'Sent up *Unity*, *Claribel*, *Assyrian*, and *Golden Gain*.'

from 'Mine Sweepers' by Rudyard Kipling

Chick, Ted, George
Three Tiffies

and a Sweeper

ACKNOWLEDGEMENTS

I am indebted to the staff of the Pentland Press for their high standard of professionalism in producing this book.

In particular my thanks go to the Editorial Director, Mr Anthony Phillips, for his overwhelming encouragement and support; and also to the Publishing Manager, Mrs Mary Denton, for her suggestions and for cheerfully putting up with some of my way-out demands.

Finally, I would like to thank my old shipmate and friend Vice Admiral Sir Louis Le Bailly for recommending the Pentland Press, the publisher of his anthology of hope, fun and despair, *Old Loves Return*.

FOREWORD

by

Vice Admiral Sir Louis Le Bailly KBE, CB, DL Hon DSc(Plymouth)
C Eng, FIMechE, FIMarE, FInstPet.

I was greatly complimented to be asked to write a Foreword to this very entertaining book. Mr Deeble and I were shipmates in the early days of the Second World War. He came to us, I seem to recall, straight from training. At any rate he shared with me the hazardous task of taking a new small cruiser from the builder's yard to the open and mine and submarine infested North Sea on machinery which up to then had only been turned slowly alongside the builder's yard on the Tyne. Thanks to the 'tiffies' all went well, and we scuttled up the swept channel to Rosyth at full speed.

Mr Deeble quotes Kipling as to the functions of a 'tiffy', the slang for that corps of craftsmen, Engine Room Artificers, unique to the Royal Navy. It was they who kept the Fleet ready for action in the First World War, not alongside in harbour as the enemy so comfortably was but in the stormy wastes of Scapa Flow. It was their sons and grandsons who performed the same feat from the Arctic to the Pacific in the Second World War.

Mr Deeble's next period of service, during which he became fully qualified and after leaving *Naiad*, included those terrible sagas escorting merchant ships under air, surface and submarine attack in sub-zero temperatures from the UK to Murmansk, a run where so many naval and merchant sailors perished in the freezing seas when their ships were sunk.

From there Alf, if I may call him that because as one reads one feels that one knows him as a person, and because by this stage he was showing his worth, was sent to Canada to stand by the new class of Algerine minesweepers. There he and his friends were beset by many problems, even to the extent that they had to find outside work 'after hours' to pay for the higher cost of living in Canada.

Toronto is a long way from the sea and the journey down the St Lawrence was fraught. It must be quite a feat to take a vessel of 1,200 tons, 225 ft. long and 11 ft. draft through several rapids, and HMS *Clinton* did not escape unscathed. All the skills for which artificers are famed were needed to reach Halifax for repair. And then to war.

A rough passage of the North Atlantic was followed by the fitting of minesweeping gear and a work-up before sailing for the Mediterranean and 'Operation Dragoon'. Minesweeping is one of the most hazardous of naval operations and men who have served in sweepers have to be very 'special'. The constant threat as a sweeper takes her place in a minefield requires a steady nerve and never more so than when 'down below', where fate, when damaged, chooses between being parboiled, incinerated or drowned.

Happily the author survived when *Clinton*'s turn came and it was largely due to his efforts that she finally reached Piraeus albeit without a bow; and as so often occurred credit for her safety bypassed the 'Man around the Engine'. Piraeus in December 1944 was an interesting and dangerous time. But there came a visit by Winston Churchill, alive as always to the real dangers of war, and his handshake is something of which Mr Deeble is clearly still proud.

There have been a good many books lately of personal recollections of the war at sea. But Mr Deeble's provides a flavour of what it all looked like, of the appalling hardships encountered, of the 'ups' and the 'downs' of the men so well described by Churchill in the House of Commons in February 1940.

I wish this afternoon to pay my tribute, here in the House of Commons, to the Engineering Branch of the Royal Navy and ask the House to join me so that these many thousands of faithful, skilful, untiring engineers may learn, as they will learn, that we here in London understand what they have done and are doing and that we admire their work and thank them for it. We must never forget the man behind the gun, but we must also remember in these modern times the man around the engine without whom nothing could be done, who does not see the excitements of the action and does not ask how things are going, but who runs a very big chance of going down with the ship should disaster come.

Mr Deeble served in the Royal Navy through those terrible years of war. As Lord Moran, who served as a doctor in the trenches throughout the first Great War and as Churchill's physician throughout the second has written,

> The Navy is efficient and knows it is efficient . . . It is a picked Service. Of four who present themselves the Navy accepts only one . . . That a boy has set his heart on this tough service goes for something.

To qualify in those days for the Navy in the first place, and to be able later to recount his experiences from a Boy Artificer to a Chief Petty Officer, shows up the fact that Mr Deeble was worthy of that great band of Engine Room Artificers to whom the Navy and the country owed, and still owe, so much. To describe what life as a 'tiffy' was like, with a sense of humour and without any attempt to hide the hardships and problems of living in a small ship in a rough sea in which acute danger always lurked, shows something more.

In recording that the nerves of three thousand sailors broke in the war, Lord Moran also records that it is the drawn out strain of service in a small ship rather than the sharp stress of naval action that ends in defeat. Three quarters of those who were broken were serving in small ships. And in another passage which should be in front of every member of every Naval Selection Board. 'It is the man of character in peace who is the man of courage in war.'

To anyone reading this book it becomes clear that Mr Deeble qualifies on both those last counts.

Chapter 1

Two Tiffies and a Cruiser

It was a cold grey afternoon in February 1943, weather typical of the Royal Navy's Scottish anchorage at Scapa Flow, as the naval drifter pushed off from the gangway of HMS *London*. The drifter dipped and wallowed across the windswept Flow toward the mainland and Chick and Ted cast a long and thoughtful look at the dull grey camouflaged County-class cruiser which had been their abode for eighteen long months. They had joined as junior ERAs (Engine Room Artificers) under training and now they were leaving as young certified Engine Room Artificers with the rating of Chief Petty Officers.

Although they both felt a slight twinge of nostalgia at leaving some of their younger mess mates, life aboard the warship had been stressful, uncomfortable and many times impersonal. Thoughts ran through their minds about long days patrolling the relentlessly heavy seas of the Denmark Straits where for hour after hour the engines toiled to maintain a headway of eight knots. So severe was the weather in this stretch of the North Atlantic between Iceland and Greenland that sea water found its way through the ship's plating into the fuel tanks causing the boiler-room personnel to be subjected to severe burning as tongues of fire would flash across the working areas from the furnaces. Above all, they recalled the rigours of the Arctic convoys to and from Murmansk or Archangel where the sea slopped against the ship's side in a state of transformation as it turned from cold water to ice, and where the ship built up layer upon layer of ice and snow so that to the Walrus sea-plane, circling above, the

1

vessel appeared like an ice-berg: a dangerous ice-berg that could become top heavy and unstable and possibly capsize.

To prevent such a catastrophe the crew worked round the clock chipping and steaming away the ice. The weather in these latitudes was probably some of the world's worst. This in itself was a major problem in trying to escort a convoy of thirty to forty ships, but apart from that, the twenty-four hours of daylight during the Arctic summer gave no respite from the prying eyes of the enemy. The Arctic winter with its twenty-four hours of darkness proved equally dangerous. Ships would lose position, some collide, others more nervous would take no chances in the dark and fire upon enemy or friend alike.

Perhaps the incident that stood out in the memories of both the young Chiefs was 4 July 1942 when *London*, escorting the north-bound convoy PQ-17, received a most urgent signal from the Admiralty to 'Scatter the Convoy!' The result was one of the most disastrous convoys of the war. Out of an original convoy of thirty-five merchant vessels, twenty-four were sunk.

This episode lingered in the minds of many and especially the crew of the *London*. It lingered in the thoughts of Chick and Ted as the form of the *London* slowly receded into the horizon, that February 1943. Today it still haunts Ted and probably most of today's veterans of the *London*. For Ted, the ill-fated convoy of 4 July 1942 was the climax of a heart-breaking period. Immediately prior to *London* sailing to form up with convoy PQ-17, Ted had received a telegram stating that his mother had died. 'How could that be?' he thought, 'She's only forty-six!' Then the original grief gave way to an almost unbearable violent sorrow. His father was away from home serving in the submarine service, a brother was away serving with the Fleet Air Arm. That left his twelve-year-old brother (who had been previously designated as the 'Man of the House' by all). How could this boy stand up to the trauma and feeling of hopelessness as his mother lay dying in his arms from a stroke, and then, how could he cope with the awful responsibility that his mother had died during the 'Man's' watch? Ted tried desperately to get home to the funeral at least, but the Captain refused his request over and over again, coming out with the rather lame excuse that Ted was too valuable, a really laughable comment when Ted knew he was one of the most junior members of the mess and was still under training. As an afterthought, the Captain then stated that 'So many people were dying at home, that the ship's company could become dangerously depleted!'

Ted thought to himself and had an almost uncontrollable urge to shout out, loud and clear, 'Bastard!' He then went to the upper deck and cried torrents as the ship slipped her moorings and the gulls joined in with their screaming cries. His youngest brother carried the emotional scars of self-blame in silence and eventually committed suicide at a very early age: another indirect casualty of the war.

With a subdued toot from its steam whistle and the locomotive's wheels spinning fast and free, the train slowly ambled out of Thurso station. The Chiefs sank back into diagonally-opposite corner seats of the carriage. A semi-contented feeling of relaxation came over them and then an inexplicable sensation of well-being which had been slowly building since they left the ship suddenly surfaced throughout their being, for as each station, telephone pole and mile flashed by, they were getting closer and closer to home and the only ones that really cared about them: their families.

But first they must report back to the Royal Naval Barracks, Chatham, the place where they had met for the first time twenty months ago.

Chapter 2

What is a Tiffy?

Ted was the product of an indentured Marine Engineering apprenticeship of four years with a London firm of ship-repairers and boiler-makers, together with a further two years as an Engine-Room Artificer apprentice in the Royal Navy. He had become an accomplished machinist and fitter, and he had two first placed prizes from The Lords Commissioners of the Admiralty for meritorious work to prove it. One of the books, a beautifully leather-bound collection of Rudyard Kipling's writings, held a particular sense of pride and purpose for him, for contained within its pages was the piece titled 'Their Lawful Occasions' with the following lines, which Ted, throughout the years, would read over and over again:

> 'That's Mr Hinchcliffe,' said Pyecroft. 'He's what is called a first-class engine-room artificer. If you hand 'im a drum of oil an' leave 'im alone, he can coax a stolen bicycle to do typewritin'.'

Ted's training gave him a unique feeling of touch, smell and even taste for the various engineering materials. His touch became so sensitive that he could gauge the dimension of a piece of metal within one half of a thousandth of an inch and actually demonstrated this to none other than His Majesty King George VI during the sovereign's visit to the Royal Navy Mechanical Training Establishment at Rosyth in 1940. Ted was intrigued by His Majesty's intense interest as the intricacies of a micrometer were demonstrated to him.

Previous to meeting Chick for the first time, Ted had already been at sea on a Dido class cruiser, during which the warship had intercepted German convoys off the coast of Norway and had been involved in a gruelling eight-hour chase at top speed of the German cruisers *Scharnhorst* and *Gneisenau*. Unfortunately the Germans with their superior speed and more effective radar had managed to slip away.

Chick was called-up for military service in October 1940. Known professionally as Chick Henderson, his real name was Henderson Rowntree, but throughout the war, his friends and acquaintances referred to him as Chick. His career as a popular dance-band vocalist started in the mid-thirties and continued until January 1942, with such bands as that of Joe Loss and with Harry Roy's Orchestra, playing at the Café Anglais in June 1940. At the height of his career he was recording eight titles a month and was the only singer to become an international star on the strength of one record. That song was 'Begin the Beguine', which sold over a million records globally and is still selling today.

He also broadcast on the BBC's *Navy Mixture* and appeared on the wartime shows of ENSA. Prior to embarking on a singing career, Chick had served an engineering apprenticeship with the Central Marine Engine Works in his home town of Hartlepool.

It was therefore logical that the Navy should utilise his practical engineering training and, having successfully passed the trade test for a fitter and turner, he was entered as an acting fourth class Engine-Room Artificer with the rating of a Petty Officer.

Whilst waiting to be drafted to some ship or establishment, Chick and Ted were employed in the repair shops of Chatham Naval Dockyard.

Each morning the repair party detail would form-up under the charge of Chick, he being the senior tiffy (Artificer). At the appropriate command, he would march us smartly off through the barracks. Once through the barrack gates and into the dockyard and beyond the prying eyes of officialdom, Chick would give vent to his built-in big band beat, and the monotonous military left, right, left, would turn into a swinging saunter. The dockyard mateys would laugh and clap as the beat went on. To them it probably looked like a re-enactment of Jimmy Stewart's film version of Captain Glenn Miller's army band style of marching.

Once assembled in the workshop, the duty Chief ERA would designate to each artificer a particular job. The job could consist of a new engineering component to be manufactured or an old part to be repaired. Chick and Ted loved to be given a blueprint of a large mild-steel coupling or shaft or some other major component: that is, something they could sink their teeth into. They both felt a satisfying challenge to their machining abilities as they watched the sweet-smelling steam rise from the lathe tool as the coolant poured onto it and the continuous length after length of corkscrewing swarf wormed its way down the length of the lathe and returned back into the catchment pan below.

On occasions during the evening hours in the mess, Chick would entertain by singing a number of the songs made famous by him. Most nights however when he was not required for duty he went home to wife and daughter in London and for the majority of the times when he was listed for duty, Ted would substitute for him for the cost of 'sippers' (a sip of Chick's daily tot of rum). So while Chick would be sleeping in the luxury of his four-poster, Ted would be tossing and turning on his hammock, stretched out on the concrete floor under the mess wash-basins.

Apart from the constant nightly air-raid warnings and the drone of the enemy planes making their way to bomb London, little damage was experienced from the German aircraft during this time, with the exception of one bomb that landed on a toilet and killed the artificer occupying it.

The two mess-mates even found time to play cricket during the glorious summer weather of that year. Ted recalled the irony of one occasion during one beautiful hot September afternoon. Whilst waiting for his turn to bat, he was lying on his back looking at the white puffy clouds slowly drifting across a bright blue sky criss-crossed by aircraft vapour trails. The Royal Air Force was in mortal combat with the German Luftwaffe two miles above him. Every now and then the summer hum of insects would be interrupted by the distant rat-tat-tat of aircraft machine-gun fire. That evening the newspaper headlines would, like cricket scores, report the number of planes brought down by each side during this one day in the 'Battle of Britain'.

During September, London was attacked practically every night by a force averaging two hundred bombers and it almost became monotonous to hear the same old remark exclaimed in the Tiffies' mess as the undulating drone of the German bombers passed overhead: 'Poor old London's getting it again.'

On the last day of September, HMS *London*, not London, was getting Chick and Ted. They had been drafted to the eight-inch County cruiser now lying at Scapa Flow; and so began their eighteen months' companionship at sea.

Chapter 3

Up the Line

And so it was that they found themselves this February morning in 1943 back amongst the familiar red-brick buildings of the Royal Naval Barracks, Chatham. The numbers of blue-collared sailors and petty officers in their fore and aft rigs seemed to have increased considerably. The pavement on the right-hand side of the main road into the barracks was still free of ratings and still reserved for the exclusive use of officers. Ratings below that of petty officers still doubled smartly across the parade ground and ratings who forgot or ignored the order soon almost had their eardrums blasted out by the bellowing voice of some GI (Gunnery instructor) looking out for such infractions from high above on the overlooking balcony.

Chick and Ted found things much the same in the ERAs' Mess; the same old Chief and Senior ERAs seemed to be holding on to their positions in the mess and office. These landlubbers richly deserved their title of barrack-stanchions by the seagoing members.

The new arrivals found their elevation to Chief Petty Officer status did entitle them to some minor privileges. Ted could now sling his hammock within the comparative comfort of the mess instead of laying it out on the bone-chilling concrete floor under the wash basins. Such mundane comforts at this time were given little thought; leave and ten glorious days to do whatever one's heart desired was the stimulant that invaded their being for the following twenty-four hours.

Next day the dream came true; they were handed travel warrants, pay, ration allowance and a notice when to report back. They had a drink together at Victoria Station. Chick took a taxi to his home in Ealing and Ted taxied to King's Cross railway station.

Once home Chick quickly changed into his civvies and along with his actress wife, Pamela Stirling, constantly partied with their friends in the West End. He also appeared a number of times with the dance band at the Café Anglais and at other top London clubs. As though determined to escape from the war and the nightly bombings, they would socialise and dance until the wee hours of the morning at a number of the subterranean night clubs where food and drink, normally unobtainable in wartime Britain, were ever present at a price.

Ted's wife Senta was also in uniform as an Intelligence Officer with the RAF at a remote station atop a high headland overlooking the North Sea at Scarborough. And so it was to Scarborough he went. It wasn't always possible to get leave together in wartime and on two previous occasions they had been disappointed. This time the god of war smiled and after fulfilling one or more nights of duty, she was free.

They decided on making that wonderful old city of York their home from home. It was only just prior to HMS *London* sailing on the ill-fated PQ-17 convoy that they had married, and so the wonderment and desires of youth and love were very much alive; and it was spring. Senta's well-tailored uniform did not detract from her femininity and Ted felt proud to show her off.

Their hotel close to the Minster was a fine sandstone-sculptured building with the interior lined in beautiful oak panels and the morning breakfast set in the dining room as the sun broke through induced a feeling of tranquillity and well-being as they started each precious day.

The crooked narrow streets of the old city were lined with quaint shops, historical houses, fountains and statues. The couple loved browsing through the old-established book shops and among one of them found a beautiful calligraphic plaque, coloured in red, black and gold lettering, of Rudyard Kipling's poem 'If'.

They spent a number of sunny afternoons rowing on the tranquil River Ouse, with an occasional stop to lie together on the grassy bank. It was during one of these lay-overs that Ted, in the midst of a smooching session, was interrupted by a high-pitched female voice, screaming, 'This is private property!' Turning his head he saw a tall, elderly woman peering down at him. He muttered a quiet 'Bugger off!' and renewed his amorous activities. However the virago pressed her attack home with her walking stick into Ted's shoulder blade and repeated, 'This is private property, and I'm the wife of the Archbishop of York!' It flashed through Ted's mind to reply by shouting, 'And I'm King George VI!' However, realising the lady might well be who she claimed to be, he decided to cast-off for quieter waters.

Alas, the days of bliss and contentment soon flashed by and that awful nagging feeling of separation and returning to the hard and impersonal world of war began to invade their being. That last evening they tried to stretch out every minute as they slowly strolled back to the railway station. They stopped off at the last pub, which was overflowing with service men and women and a few civilians. The talk was loud and excited and the pair found themselves shouting at each other in order to hear. The air was thick with tobacco smoke and the faint chimes of Big Ben coming from the wireless could barely be heard. Then the BBC announcer proclaimed, 'This is the nine o'clock news, and here is the Prime Minister.'

A hushed silence fell over the entire assembly as Mr Churchill in one of his many Sunday evening talks brought the British people and their allies up-to-date with both the good and the bad news about the war. He consoled us with the fact that the enemy in Europe and Asia had been driven to the defensive; the battle of Stalingrad had turned the tide in the favour of Russia; Australia and New Zealand had become free from the threat of invasion and Allied naval power was becoming supreme on and under the surface. However he warned that the Battle of the Atlantic was still a dominating factor, everything depended on its outcome and that vigilance could never be relaxed. Raising his voice in a typical 'Once more into the breach, dear friends' kind of rallying call, he urged us to renew our spirits and press forward until victory was finally ours.

With Mr Churchill's voice still ringing in their ears, the intensity of the babble increased throughout the bar; however, the voices were more excited and confident. The Prime Minister seemed to have injected a stimulant equal to any of that behind the bar.

Leaving the warmth and light of the pub, the couple snuggled together against the cool damp evening air as they stumbled along slowly trying to get their eyes accustomed to the darkness. The station was dimly lit and uniformed figures, some carrying rifles, some kit bags, suitcases, hammocks and backpacks, filled both platforms either side of the tracks. The train for Scarborough pulled in, a faint light fell across the platform as some carriage doors were opened, the couple gave each other a last lingering kiss, the carriage door slammed closed and Senta was off back to the RAF.

Ted paced the crowded platform for another hour thinking how very different he had felt just ten days ago and wondering when if ever this bloody war would be over. A faint light at the north end of the station ushered in the arrival of his train and he too was off back to the war.

Chapter 4

The Three Meet

Next morning Ted joined the mass of navy-blue-uniformed sailors surging through the main gate of the barracks. The usual welcoming committee of 'mouth and gaitered' regulating staff of Chiefs, POs and other ratings were yelling, 'Come on, move it!', and 'You over there! Put your cap on straight!' and 'Ordinary Seaman So & So, report to the office at the double!' And so it went on; they almost felt that they had committed a crime and were being herded back into prison. But the guards were not prison guards, they only acted like them.

Ted tried to shut out the vulgar ravings of officialdom and petty power from his ears and mind and slowly made his way to the mess for breakfast.

At nine o'clock that morning he and a goodly number of other ERAs had to report to the Drafting Office in the main Drill Hall. They huddled together outside the open window of the Drafting Office and awaited their particular name to be called. The office was manned by Wrens (Woman Royal Navy Service ratings) with a sprinkling of Chiefs, old POs, Barrack Stanchions and a few officers.

As each name was called out in alphabetical order, the tiffy would mount the three steps and present himself at the window. The PO on the other side would either ask him to report in a week's time or would hand him a draft chit. The draft chit would indicate that he had been designated to join a certain ship or establishment and would give a date when to report back to the office, at which time he would be despatched with the rest of the draft to his next tour of duty.

As each ERA stepped down from the window, his oppos (special friends) would surround him and excitedly ask, 'What yer got?' Most hoped that for another week or more they had escaped the draft, for it meant that they had another chance to get 'up-the-line' (anywhere away from the Navy in Britain or Eire). On the other hand, if their luck had run out, at least they hoped their friends were going to accompany them to their new 'home'.

Ted descended the drafting office steps with a puzzled look on his face.

'Well, what yer got?' Chick queried as he pushed his way forward.

'Search me!' replied Ted as he stared at the bold capitals on the chit: ALG/C1. 'What the hell does that mean?' he muttered.

He waited for Chick's turn. As Chick approached from the steps, he threw up his arms in disbelief, remarking, 'I've got the same bloody thing.' They were overheard by another artificer who joined them and, in his excited north-country dialect, yelled, 'What sort of ship is ALG bloody C1, anyhoo?'

Chick mimicked his accent and replied, 'I doon't na!' The Geordie was George Mowat.

All three eventually wandered slowly back to the mess, all the time puzzling in their minds what this strange draft could be. Ted convinced himself that it was a nice cushy shore establishment in Algeria and he could already imagine great runs ashore down the Casbah. The others kept calling out the names of ships and establishments whose name started with the letter A, but to no avail.

Chapter 5

Humanity, Navy Style

Whilst standing round in the drill hall to see if any others came up with the same draft, Ted became interested in the treatment to which some junior ratings were being subjected at the drafting station further down the hall.

He had recognised four stokers from his first sea-going ship, HMS *Naiad*. All four had survived her sinking in the Mediterranean in the spring of 1942 and here they were again, newly arrived in barracks after surviving yet another sinking. Actually, one of the stokers had now survived three of them.

The lads had arrived before dawn after an overnight train journey from Liverpool, having been landed there from the destroyer which had plucked them from the Atlantic. It was now eleven o'clock in the morning and the weary bunch of survivors had been kept standing in line in the drill hall ever since marching from Chatham railway station at 5 a.m. As yet they had received no food and what comfort or relaxation they might crave from a cigarette was denied by 'No Smoking' signs in eight-inch-high letters, printed on the walls, while behind the drafting office windows, Officers, Chiefs, POs and Wrens were puffing away at their favourite brands during intervals between sipping their tea.

It infuriated Ted to watch how this tired, hungry group of men were treated like undesirables, especially by the Wrens. A number of them, some of them former office and bank managers, foremen and store owners, had been through hell and were fit candidates for treatment at trauma centres and yet these ex shop assistants, office girls, waitresses and maids, now Wrens, processed the men like some sub-species, devoid of human emotions. It was almost sickening to witness the transformation in these girls' behaviour when approached by an officer. It was almost as though the ugly stepmother had become Cinderella at the ball.

Ted was about to return to his own group, when the drill hall reverberated to the bark of a burly, red-faced Master-at-Arms.

'You two! What do you think this is, a bloody holiday camp? Get off yer arses and get fallen-in at the double!' he yelled. The two young seamen abruptly overcame their weariness of the past days and leaped up from the drafting office steps to join their shipmates in line.

The incident reminded Ted of his first run-in with a Master-at-Arms (ship's chief policeman). He had presented himself at the Naval recruiting office in Whitehall in late 1938 to take the educational test prescribed for Artificers (special entry) for admittance into the Royal Navy. Part of the test covered the first rules of arithmetic. Since he was already within one year of earning his Higher National Certificate in Mechanical Engineering, the test was to him a cakewalk. Within a few minutes he handed the completed test to the proctor (a stern-faced Master-at-Arms).

The Master, after consulting what was obviously the answer list, returned and slammed down the test paper in front of Ted, exclaiming, 'Yer failed!' The paper was slashed with X's against each answer and a big 0 at the bottom.

Ted couldn't believe his ears or his eyes as he looked at the 0. Confident that there was some mistake he asked to look at the answer sheet. He was refused. He then asked to see the recruiting officer or some other authority. Try as he might he was refused. A Captain of Marines appeared in the room and enquired what all the noise was about.

The Master replied, 'We've got a stroppy recruit 'ere, Sir, who thinks he knows the answers better than what we does.'

'Bring him and the papers into my office, Master!' The officer looked at the papers and eventually said, 'Well, Master, what's the trouble?'

'Well,' said the Master, 'take for example question one. The answer is an 'arf, he's got nought dot five; and 'ere again, number two, the answer is a quarter and he's got nought dot two five.'

The officer then turned to the Master saying, 'But his answer zero decimal point five and zero decimal point two five mean the same thing as a half and a quarter respectively.'

The Marine then proceeded to put a tick against the answers with a final 100% mark at the bottom of the page.

'Put him down with a 100% for arithmetic, Master,' said the officer and instantly dismissed the occupants of his office with a 'That's all.'

All during the writing part of the examination Ted could feel the piercing glare of the Master's eyes upon him. However, little did the Master know that Ted could not have cared less, for until he signed his final papers he could walk away from the Navy.

During his final phase of the examination, Ted was disturbed by a shouting and crying match between the Master-at-Arms and a very young seaman recruit. The boy had forgotten to address him as 'Sir' and he had a number of dirty, filthy blots on his examination paper, observed the Master. The more the boy cried, the more the Master lashed him with demeaning phrases like, 'You're a disgrace to your country,' and 'God help you if you ever get into the Navy, which I doubt.'

Ted couldn't stand this treatment of a terrified human being any longer and with a bellow that startled both boy and Master, yelled out, 'Why don't you leave him alone, you bloody great bully?' The whole office went silent as junior ratings buried their heads into whatever work they had on their desks. The boy's tears had stopped as though turned off by a faucet, as the Master smartly turned, walked over and stood over Ted, breathing heavily like a heated bull. He poured tirade after tirade upon Ted. However Ted continued to make him more outraged by totally ignoring him and carrying on with his writing examination. Inwardly however he was a little concerned that the seething mass towering over him might suddenly have a heart attack. The situation slowly simmered down as some officers started to criss-cross the room to their various offices.

With Ted's papers marked and given a passing mark, the Master called him over to his desk and announced, 'And now I'm going to take you in to see one of the top engineers in the Navy, so mind your lip. Is that clear?' Ted made no comment or facial movement.

The so-called 'top engineer' turned out to be a white-haired, rather fatherly Lieutenant-Commander, his well-worn uniform jacket looking as though a few seas had washed over it, for the gold buttons had traces of verdigris embedded in them and the occasional gold thread hung from the rings around the cuffs. The purple distinguishing cloth between the two and a half rings had faded. Nevertheless, he made Ted feel comfortable and inspired him with the thought that perhaps life could be bearable and exciting working under such men.

Looking over Ted's papers, the officer repeated Ted's surname and asked, 'Did you have a relation in the Navy during the Great War in submarines?'

'Yes,' replied Ted. 'My dad was a Chief Electrical Artificer in them.'

'Well, what do you know!' exclaimed the two and a half ringer. 'We were together on the *Vulcan*.'

The officer then wanted to know all about Ted's father and ended up walking Ted to the door of his office with his arm round Ted's shoulder. The scene probably did not improve the Master's feelings towards Ted and as a parting shot at him, he mumbled, 'And I hope those Royal Marines at Rosyth will kick the bloody living daylights out of yer when you get up there.'

Actually, during Ted's training aboard HMS *Caledonia* at Rosyth, he never did come in contact with any marines but he did come in contact with the *Caledonia*'s Master-at-Arms Davies who turned out to be one of the finest gentlemen he had ever met, as was the mess President Chief ERA Brown. Master-at-Arms Davies was young for his rating, was good-looking and athletic, but was also a strict disciplinarian. The tiffy boys knew this and though they might rant and rave about the punishment meted out to them, they knew inwardly that it was just. Davies would throw himself into their sporting activities and was always ready to give some fatherly advice when needed. He really was part of the glue that held the establishment together.

Ted and his classmates felt a genuine sadness at having to say goodbye to the Master and Chief ERA Brown as the young ERAs left to join the fleet. Unfortunately the tyrannical behaviour that Ted had experienced at the Whitehall recruiting office pervaded the boy seamen's establishment aboard HMS *Caledonia*.

He couldn't believe that early in 1939, POs were still allowed openly to strike the face of these boys, and with officers in full attendance, some of the boys' ages being from fourteen and a half to sixteen years. Ted thought of the level of willingness, co-operation, industry and pride the instructors, Master at Arms Davies and Chief ERA Brown, had brought out in the apprentices without resorting to the archaic methods applied to the seamen boys. So strong was the desire among some boys to escape this inhumane treatment that two committed suicide, five escaped through the sewer system into the middle of Rosyth and a further six took a ship's whaler from its moorings and rowed down the Firth of Forth and out into the North Sea. They were caught and returned by a destroyer.

As Ted made his way back from the crowd of survivors in the drill hall to his own group, he wondered how many in the Admiralty had taken Nelson's last prayer seriously: 'And may humanity after victory be the predominant feature of the British Fleet.'

Chapter 6

The Mystery of Draft ALG/C1

ALG/C1: what did it mean? The three tiffs wondered, then dismissed the thought as they realised that only two days remained before venturing upon the mysterious draft. Chick off-duty charged up to London on the first evening; the second night, though designated for duty, Ted substituted for him and so up the line he went again. Ted spent his last night ashore in Chatham wandering aimlessly about and occasionally dropping into a pub, until watching the level of beer slowly lowering in the glass got boring and his stomach became so uncomfortably full. With nothing else to do he headed back to barracks and his hammock.

George, the new member of the trio, didn't appear to have any ties and sought relaxation or excitement, whichever the case was, wherever he found it and for his last two nights of freedom he spent socialising with anybody and everybody having mutual interests, be it in the grill of the Strand Hotel, the saloon bar at Victoria Station or the Elephant and Castle in south London. Wherever his runs ashore took him, it was a safe bet that he would return to ship or base in a state of disarray and penniless.

Before being called up for national service, George had served his apprenticeship and eventually became a journeyman fitter and turner in the locomotive building shops of the North-Eastern Railway in Darlington. He was immensely strong, of medium height with broad shoulders and a huge chest. It was therefore of little wonder that during his years with the railway he had held many championship titles for boxing together with cups. During a fight, be it in the ring or during a brawl, his face with its ruddy and scarred complexion, together with his broken nose, would take on a defiant grin as his brilliant blue eyes followed every movement. His attack was devastating and within seconds he could completely disorientate his opponent with a barrage of shattering blows.

All three tiffies presented themselves at the drafting office as noted on their draft chits. Chick and George looked all the worst for wear after their night in London. Ted wasn't much better after the constant night bombing round the Medway towns. As they loaded their hammocks, kit-bags, suitcases and toolboxes onto the lorry, they kept asking the drafting Chief where they were going and what ALG/C1 meant. The only satisfaction they got was that the lorry was taking them to Chatham station. That much they had guessed for themselves.

Early in the afternoon they reached Victoria Station, London. Now where to? Ted recognised the various parts of London as yet another lorry headed toward the late afternoon sun. It was wartime so all signs had been removed, but he was familiar with King's Cross and Euston stations as they rumbled by. Shortly after, the lorry stopped at some other station. Ted knew the next one past Euston had to be St Pancras and St Pancras was the terminal of the London Midland and Scottish Railway. Could it be Liverpool they were heading for?

It was becoming dark and George in his rather direct manner let vent to what most in the railway carriage were thinking. 'Let's get out of here quick before those bloody Jerries start bombing!' he exclaimed, making himself comfortable in a corner seat opposite an ATS girl. There were two other Army girls in the compartment and as the conversation increased in intensity, Ted thought how different these girls were in comparison with those snobbish, self-righteous Wren bitches in Chatham Barracks.

The train raced on and after an hour or so the compartment was thick with tobacco smoke as the three artificers passed out their duty-free cigarettes to all and sundry.

With a number of head-jolting jerks, the train came to a halt. It was a station. Lifting the corner of the blackout blinds, the occupants could see masses of service people moving about and members of the WVS

(Women's Voluntary Service) handing out cups of tea and sandwiches.
'What station is this?' Chick asked. He received no reply. All three
crossed the platform to a WVS tea wagon. A lady wearing the standard
grey felt hat with its green band and badge on front poured them each a
cup and they, as was the unconscious habit, took turns in stirring their
tea with a spoon tied securely to the wagon with a piece of string. The
stirring was an exercise in futility, for not only was there no sugar in the
tea to be dissolved, the spoon only made the tea colder. Maybe it was a
case of nostalgia and reminded them of the good old days before the war.

There was no doubt about the WVS lady's accent. It was definitely
Lancastrian and speaking to an ARP (Air Raid Patrol) warden standing
close by, Ted learnt that the station was Manchester. The warden also
said that Manchester had had a bad air raid that night but it was Liverpool
that really bore the brunt of the Luftwaffe's reign of destruction. The
smell of burning wood and dust filled the air and clouds of blue smoke
occasionally blotted out the early morning sun as the train pulled out of
the station.

Just after midday, the train came to a grinding halt. It was another
station. Ted had been anxiously peering out at the countryside for miles
back because it looked familiar. The station convinced him that this was
Border country. His home town was in the Borders and the station he
recognised as Carlisle. As the trio headed for the station refreshment room,
Ted let them know that their probable destination was now Glasgow.
However, that knowledge didn't help in solving the mystery of ALG/C1.

Sure enough, there was no doubt about their next stop. What with the
sprawling suburbs, the size of the station and the broad West Scottish
accent of the porters, it was indeed Glasgow. The train-weary trio made
their way across the bustling platform to the naval section of the RTO's
(Railway Transportation Officer's) office. Together with all their gear
they were escorted to yet another section of the station and another train.
Their compartment was already occupied by four or five young to middle-
aged women who in their Glaswegian accent welcomed them with,
'Cummen alang, Jack, mak yersells cumfy.'

The women, attired in working trousers and with various coloured scarves kept in place by headbands, told the three sailors that they were ammunition and shipyard workers on their way to their jobs. They then broke out into singing the popular song of the day, 'Don't know where, don't know when, but I'm sure we'll meet again.'

As the last note faded away, one young, well-painted girl suddenly pointed at Chick and excitedly screamed, 'Hi! aren't you the fella what use'tah sing wi' a band on Sauchiehall Street?'

The rest of the females suddenly became silent and stared at the object of the pointed finger. George then burst forth with, 'Aye, that's wor Chick Henderson of yer know, 'Begin the Beguine!'

Chick cringed, but too late, the cat was out of the bag. With the celebrity amongst them the working lassies demanded that he gave them a song and so Chick gave forth with his 'Begin the Beguine', then, demanding more and more, the females were not satisfied until their station was reached. They were well-served, for they had also heard, 'My Prayer', 'When the lights go on again all over the world', 'Little Sir Echo' and 'The White Cliffs of Dover'.

As the train pulled out of the station, they continued to walk, then run alongside the compartment, singing, waving and throwing a final kiss as the platform ended their advance.

Miraculously, the events of the past hour or so had rejuvenated the tiffs from their previous feeling of train-travel weariness. The working girls had stated they worked at Port Glasgow, so obviously the train was running west alongside the south bank of the Clyde. Approximately a quarter of an hour after leaving Port Glasgow, the train stopped and a rating from the RTO's office advised the trio that this was the end of the line and directed them to a waiting bus. Barely had the bus been underway than it stopped at a jetty on the river. Looming way out in the middle of the river was the huge outline of a liner painted in her dull grey war paint. George let forth with, 'It's the *Queen Mary*!'

'No,' replied Ted, 'It's the *Queen Elizabeth*.' He could see this leviathan only had two funnels and he knew the *Mary* had three.

They loaded their gear onto the tender, one of many such craft continually plying between the shore and the Cunarder. As the tender's head and stern lines were secured, her rubber fenders squeaked and squealed against the hull of the liner as the incoming tide swirled and eddied between the vessels. The servicemen took a giant stride from the tender onto one of the lower decks of the liner through a set of open water-tight doors in the ship's side.

Before stepping off the tender, Ted strained his neck upwards to view the immense height of the wall of steel that towered above, then, lowering his vision, he was awed by how far the *Elizabeth*'s grey hull stretched both fore and aft. Even then he realised that many more yards of her length were obscured from his view as the ship's form curved in towards the stem and stern.

The reason for Ted's interest in the super-ship's dimensions was not just factual, but he was trying to imagine the scene when, in October 1942, the *Elizabeth*'s sister ship, the 83,000 ton *Queen Mary*, had knifed through her escorting cruiser, the 4,200 ton HMS *Curacao* at 28.5 knots. The cruiser had sunk within minutes with the loss of 331 lives.

Among the 331 were five of his classmates from his days under training at HMS *Caledonia*. They had died a horrible death whilst on duty in the engine and boiler rooms with flesh ripped away by super-heated steam, burnt by fire and impaled by the razor-sharp edges of torn steel plates. If any had survived this, which is doubtful, they would finally have succumbed to hypothermia and drowned. During an enquiry into the collision, an artificer who had joined HMS *Naiad* with Ted and who had been rescued by an escorting destroyer, testified that while he was on watch in the after engine room, the steering engine of the cruiser had been fully functional right up to the moment of impact.

Ironically, way back in October 1942, Ted had been returning to HMS *London* anchored off Greenock and noticed the *Queen Mary* also at anchor. She had a tremendous gash in her bows. Ted had thought the gash looked like the jaws of a gigantic shark. Little did he know at that time that those jaws had killed five of his classmates plus another 326 men.

Chapter 7

Westward Ho!

The atmosphere inside the giant ship was warm. A variety of smells drifted throughout the passages and stairways. One could distinguish the acrid smell of fuel oil, new paint and hot steam pipes, and the odour of vegetables from the provision chambers. There were also the typical shipboard noises of ventilation fans, the hiss of steam and the gurgle of water as they flowed through the maze of pipes, the hum of generator engines and the clang of feet ascending and descending steel stairs, plus the occasional orders and messages relayed over the ship's speaker system.

The *Queen Elizabeth* was manned on the deck and engine side by a British crew and since the captain was an officer in the RNR (Royal Naval Reserve) the vessel flew the Blue Ensign. The hotel services, food and accommodation for troops and other passengers were under the management of the United States Army.

And so it was that Chick, Ted and George were directed to their accommodation which had been a first class cabin on the upper deck. However all furnishings had been removed from the cabin and the bare, empty and now stark space had been filled wall to wall with bunk beds, four tiers high. One corner was fitted out as a salt water shower with barely enough room to turn round in. In a very short time, each bed in the space had been designated to an Army Sergeant-Major, an RAF Flight Sergeant or a Navy Chief.

It was late afternoon and it became obvious that the ship was being prepared for sea. Over the Tannoy system the Chief Officer directed that all non-crew should retire to their quarters and the crew should 'Darken Ship'. The ship's deck then started to bounce to a slow undulating rhythm as the anchor was being hauled in and each cable link bedded down into the snugs of the windlass. After a few minutes the bouncing stopped, then, as the propellers bit the water, the ship gave a shudder then a surge as the massive hull pushed the water away from her bows. She was under way.

The gold and red rays of the setting sun made a beautiful scene of land and water that was worthy of any painter's brush as the great ship rounded Kempock and Cloch Points and moved out into the ever widening Firth of Clyde.

Across the Tannoy system came the call that all the passengers were waiting for, including the three artificers, 'Dinner is now being served!' At a slow jog the three made their way along the top deck and down numerous stairs to the main dining area four decks down. The area was immense with dozens of long tables with chairs either side occupying the whole space. The smell of food and the food itself was out of this world for each and every British serviceman; and meals became by far the highlight of the day.

The American Army caterers and cooks spared no effort to process the best food and dishes that America had to offer. The variety and quantity was well above what any of the British could remember even before the war years. Apart from the meals, the dining area gave forth a feeling of well-being for it was well-lit, flowers in vases adorned the tables and the best of American music was played throughout the meals. The trio took to lingering there and drinking cup after cup of coffee.

That first night on board, the three men wandered onto the upper deck at about ten o'clock. The ship was well down the Firth of Clyde now and the land they could just make out on their starboard side was probably the Island of Arran. After a turn round the deck they decided to turn in. Ted had managed to get the lowest bunk while Chick took the next one above him. George was off in a far corner of the quarters on the topmost bunk. With the day's activities behind them, a hearty dinner, the sea air and the ever increasing throb of the propellers, they soon fell into a deep sleep.

Next morning the Tannoy located just over George's head awoke him with, 'Breakfast will be served in half an hour.' Climbing down from the high perch, he shook the other two from their sleep with a repeat of the piped notice. As Ted's feet hit the deck he stumbled and fell back into the bunk. Still sleepy and a little dazed he wondered what had happened and then realised the ship was now pitching and rolling as she moved out into the open sea.

Chick was now awake and the three took turns in using the shower. Ted gave a scream as the cold seawater struck his back. Rub as he might he failed to get a lather from the salt water soap and after drying himself with a stiff, rough towel, his body felt sticky. In fact he felt less refreshed than he did before showering. He wasn't alone in his feeling. The complaint was common among all users of the salt-water showers aboard.

A steady rain blew into their faces as they stepped out and onto the wet deck. They hesitated as each strove to gain his sea-legs. There was no land in sight but well out on the starboard bow was a cruiser. Closer in, about half a mile away on either beam, was a destroyer. They were obviously the great ship's escort. From the *Elizabeth*'s upper deck the vessel didn't appear to be moving at any great speed. However Ted had only to look at the enormous white wake churning upwards from the barely visible stern of the destroyers to realise that the liner was doing at least 28 knots and probably more since the destroyers seemed to be slowly falling back.

The smell of brewing coffee was everywhere as the three made their way down and along to the dining area. Most passengers were already having breakfast and there was a distinct increased level of conversation and laughter, no doubt brought about by a good night's sleep and the satisfying meal before them.

On each table at every place-setting was a plate with three boxes of various cereals. Along the middle of the tables at intervals of six feet were four half-gallon glass jugs filled with milk, or tomato, orange and grapefruit juice. Alongside them were smaller containers of corn and maple syrup. Between the jugs were placed baskets of rolls, croissants, various breads and several varieties of jams and jellies in small jars.

Waiters constantly passed up and down between the tables serving coffee, tea, scrambled, poached, fried and boiled eggs, sausage, ham, bacon, fried tomatoes, fried and mashed potatoes, pancakes and waffles. Set aside at the exit from the dining area was a table containing several baskets of fresh fruit for the passengers to take or leave at their will. Throughout the ship in typical US fashion were coffee dispensing machines constantly ready to serve all.

Breakfast over, Ted and Chick wandered off to a lounge at the after end of the weather deck. The lounge contained a number of small tables and seats, two beverage dispensing machines and a jukebox. The box was giving forth with Dinah Shore singing 'Stormy Weather'. 'Hell, I hope not!' thought Ted as a can of Coca-Cola slid off the table onto the deck. Ted bent down and took a can of root beer from the beverage machine. He'd never heard of or tasted this beverage and wondered whether it might be a substitute for beer as he knew it. One mouthful was sufficient to prove it wasn't and with a quick gulp he exclaimed, 'Bloody hell, this stuff tastes like toothpaste!' He pushed the can towards Chick, but Chick, raising his hand, said, 'No thanks.'

The can of root beer like the Coca-Cola started to quiver and rotate its way from the centre of the table towards the edge and within a minute landed on the deck. Ted realised that the whole after end of the ship's structure was vibrating and any free object was taking a walk. Turning to Chick he said, 'Do you remember that piece in the newspapers some time ago when a reporter stated that the engines of the *Queens* are so well-balanced and vibration-less that you can stand a penny on its edge on the turbine casings when the ships are at full speed?' Chick gave an affirmative nod. 'That fella certainly didn't bring his penny up here!' remarked Ted. The vibration in such a small enclosed space made comfort impossible and drove the pair out and onto the open deck.

In a cradle bolted down to the deck was the ship's tail-end propeller shaft. Ted was impressed by the sheer size of it. Wrapping his arms around the circumference he estimated it to be close to three feet in diameter. The sight of the shaft took his mind back to the days when, much slimmer and an apprentice, he was paid two shillings and sixpence to crawl into

27

the stern tube of the big Peninsula and Orient ocean liners to set up boring equipment for machining the lignum vitae propeller shaft bearing.

Still in a reminiscing mood he took hold of the stern handrails and looked down at the churning mass of white water being thrust upwards and astern by the four twenty-foot diameter, thirty-five ton propellers. These very propellers seventy to eighty feet below him had scored quarter inch deep grooves into the red-brick walls of his favourite pub, the Oldfellows Arms, and also into the sandstone walls surrounding the Duke of Northumberland's castle in Ted's home town of Alnwick. The street, aptly named Narrowgate, was the narrowest thoroughfare traversed by the lorry carrying all four propellers from Stone's foundry in Charlton, London to John Brown's shipyard on Clydebank.

Ted had an uncle who once worked as a moulder at Stones. He wondered whether the *Queen Elizabeth*'s ship's bell had been cast there. He knew that the propellers of HMS *Nelson* and the record-breaking liners *Queen Mary*, *Normandie*, and *Bremen*, together with Italy's crack liners *Rex* and *Conte di Savoia* had been.

It was noon. The destroyers had disappeared and way astern on the horizon, the faint flicker from the cruiser's aldis signalling lamp could just be seen. The *Queen* was on her own. Word had obviously got round about Chick's singing abilities for at lunch, the entertainments officer asked him if he would oblige by rendering a few songs that evening in the main lounge to the passengers. And so Chick ended up entertaining the troops every other day during the crossing.

Like the US Navy, the *Elizabeth* was 'dry'. On the second day out, however, Ted bumped into the Second Engineer Officer who, it turned out, had served his apprenticeship with Ted at Green and Silley Weir of London. The Second immediately invited Ted and Chick up to his cabin for drinks, the *Elizabeth*'s British officers not being subject to the US 'dry' law. With an open-house invitation, they would spend a pleasant relaxing hour or so each evening supping their favourite brew in the Second's cabin or the Engineer Officers' wardroom.

Eventually they learned from the Second that the ship was bound for Halifax, Nova Scotia, Canada.

'What would we be going to Canada for?' thought Ted. He knew about some of his own grammar school mates going to Canada as part of the Empire Training Scheme for RAF pilots, but what could Canada offer as regards naval training? He thought about the mysterious ALG/C1 draft code. Could the C stand for Canada? Ted felt a little guilty about not taking George along for a nightcap each evening, but thought it seemed like bad manners to sponge any more on the Second.

After just over four days zigzagging her way across the North Atlantic, the great ship tied up alongside a wharf in Halifax, her immense bulk towering over the warehouse.

Chapter 8

O! Canada by Train

It was spring, but the weather was still bitterly cold and the snow lay two to three feet thick. Ashore could be seen a number of passenger and freight trains standing among a maze of railway tracks. Great white clouds of steam rose straight up for thirty to forty feet into the frigid air. Occasionally one of the locomotives would give out a loud mournful wail from its whistle. The station was a hive of activity, the pace made higher by those trying to seek some degree of warmth from the bitter morning air. For the ERAs, that warmth was found in the railway carriage to which the Canadian RTO directed them.

Ladies from the Red Cross constantly passed backwards and forwards along the corridors of the railway carriages, offering sandwiches, cookies, cakes, pies, fruit, coffee and tea to the servicemen. Most of the food was home-made. These ladies really went all-out to make everybody feel at home. After an hour or so the train suddenly gave a huge jolt, then slowly moved out of the station. The air in the carriage was dry and hot and smelt of paint from the steam radiators. It made the mouth dry and sticky. George said that it made his mouth feel like the bottom of a bird cage. Ted thrust open the window to let in some fresh air, but immediately closed it for within seconds of the window being opened the compartment was freezing.

The train rolled along for hour after hour across the wide expanse of snow covered countryside, occasionally running alongside frozen lakes and rivers. Now and then the locomotive would let out a mournful wail as it approached a small station or sped toward a level crossing where red flashing lights at the roadside and the sound of a large clanging bell would warn pedestrians and vehicles of its approach. The glare of the snow slowly became painful to the eyes and so the passengers either closed them or turned them away from the windows.

Unlike in Britain, the stations still retained their name boards. Within the first day the train had stopped at Truro, Monitor and Van Buren. It was getting dark and the only light outside came from the reflection of the carriage lights upon the snow and from the lights of an occasional small station or village.

The atmosphere in the carriage had become worse because of the addition of cigarette smoke, so Ted decided to spend many minutes pacing the corridor outside. It was now almost twenty-four hours since leaving Halifax. The tiffies were becoming weary and uncomfortable as they constantly twisted and turned their bodies in search of a position that would give some relief to their aching muscles and joints.

It was morning and still the vast landscape beyond the carriage window was thick with snow. Then out on the right-hand side of the train appeared a tremendously wide frozen river. The train ran along the bank of the river for mile after mile, occasionally stopping at a small station. During these stops, Ted would try to relieve the monotony by opening the window even if it meant facing the freezing conditions outside.

There was generally a small group of women with children viewing the train as it pulled in. They smiled and the children would say something in high-pitched voices. Ted couldn't understand what they were saying so, putting his hand to his ear, indicated that he didn't understand. The women and children drew closer and repeated whatever they were saying. Ted then suddenly caught two or three words. They were speaking French! He quickly summoned up whatever French he had learnt at the grammar school and it seemed to get a response from the children. He managed to get across to them that he was English and to the delight of the youngest, he handed out whatever small English coinage he had in his pockets. The kids were delighted and reciprocated by dropping a few Canadian cents and five-cent pieces into his hand. The conversation proved to be difficult and after a time, he realised his Parisian French was quite different to their Canadian dialect and so the whole exercise dwindled down to mere 'Oui's' and 'Non's'. Nevertheless they all managed a shy wave as the train pulled out of the station.

The train hugged the bank of the large frozen river until about three o'clock in the afternoon. Bleak stretches of snow-covered terrain appeared on both sides of the track. For another eight hours, station after station bore a French name. Finally, at 11 p.m., the train slowed down to a crawl as it rocked and shuffled over umpteen points and curves. It was passing through a large suburban area. Eventually the brilliant lights of a major city loomed up ahead. It was Montreal.

With screeching wheels and a sudden jerk, the train came to a halt. Almost immediately, all compartment doors flew open as the occupants poured out onto the platform.

The magic of the city's lights and flashing neon signs were sights most of the British servicemen had not seen for three and a half years. Although Chick and Ted had witnessed the lights of Reykjavik, Iceland, for various periods over a year and a half whilst aboard the *London*, those sights had not thrilled them but made them nervous, for they knew those very lights provided lurking U-boats with a well-lit background against which the silhouette of Allied shipping could be plainly defined.

An announcement echoed across the station warning passengers of the newly-arrived train that it would depart in precisely one hour's time. Some of the servicemen headed for the well-stocked restaurants and lounges in the station. Others made their way into the adjoining streets and bars. Still others pursued the ladies of the night. It wasn't much of a pursuit for their catch was ready and willing and were obviously following a routine that they had perfected over many previous train arrivals.

A cold wind blew through the station as huddled figures started climbing back aboard the train. The locomotive gave three blasts of its whistle as the flow of passengers increased. The whistle gave one long blast as military police dragged drunk passengers along the platform and pushed them into compartments up and down the train. The conductor blew a prolonged blast on his whistle while waving his oil-lamp in the direction of the locomotive. Carriage doors slammed closed and with a rapid skidding of the locomotive's wheels on the tracks, the train slowly moved out of the station and into the night. Within a short time of everybody relating about their adventure in Montreal, the effects of much food, drink and exercise took over and most fell into a deep sleep. It was well past midnight.

As daylight once again lit up the countryside, snow still lay thick on both sides of the tracks. However, every now and again they could see an immense stretch of flat ice as far as the horizon. It had to be a Great Lake. The stations were now popping-up at more regular intervals and at shorter distances between. They also bore familiar English names like Newcastle, Whitby and Scarborough.

Chapter 9

Journey's End

The train moved slowly, screeching and squealing as it weaved a twisting, turning pattern through a maze of points and tracks. It was an immense rail-yard covering acres. Finally the tracks straightened out as the train slowly came to a stop in the station. The word was passed along that this was the end of the line.

The passengers bent their heads and shoulders forward as they slowly dragged their feet up an incline and into the main hall of the station. The hall was enormous with great marble columns and walls. It resembled what a Greek temple must have looked like twenty-five centuries ago. It was Toronto's Union Station. The three artificers stamped their feet in an attempt to keep warm as a biting ice-cold wind swept across the flat open spaces from the ice-covered lake to the south. They realised their clothing was no match for this weather. Ted thought that at least they used to don a balaclava and dufflecoat on Russian convoys.

Eventually they were loaded onto some Royal Canadian Navy buses. Snow was driving hard and building up on the windshield of the bus as the fast-moving wipers tried to cope with it. The exhausts from cars, buses and manhole covers swirled round like clouds of steam. The buses passed through the gates of an enormous white stone archway and stopped. Immediately beyond the gates the passengers, all British sailors, got off and were directed into a large stone building. It was HMCS (His Majesty's Canadian Ship) *York*. The white stone archway was the entrance to the Canadian National Exhibition grounds. The trio were directed to the Chief and POs' Mess and asked if they'd like breakfast. As always the answer was in the affirmative, especially for a Canadian breakfast. The Canadian cooks outdid themselves and provided whatever the new arrivals requested. Eggs prepared in their variety of ways headed the list and the British sailors showed their appreciation for a quality and quantity of food that must have been one of the highest in the world.

HMCS *York* was full of young Canadian junior ratings, mostly from small, agricultural towns and villages located hundreds of miles from the sea. The majority had never seen the sea, except in pictures and at the movies. To Ted they seemed so innocent, yet so enthusiastic to experience life at sea. They followed the trio around like fans attending celebrities. All the time they asked questions about what it was like to be on destroyers, cruisers or battleships and what action the three men had seen.

Ted felt a little embarrassed at all the hero worship and wished he could have set a better example. His appearance and uniform had suffered since leaving Chatham and here he was surrounded by vibrant, young, enthusiastic boys in spotless, well-tailored uniforms. He felt even more embarrassed at being addressed as 'Sir' and in some cases at even being saluted, these being marks of respect to which he as a senior rating was not entitled. He knew that the Canadian Navy had very few large warships and that the majority of these young eager beavers would be destined for destroyers or corvettes. Life aboard these small vessels on convoy duty in the North Atlantic would be no picnic, especially for junior ratings; it was common knowledge that the corvettes were said to roll on a wet blanket. They would find themselves crowded into living quarters with seventy or more of their shipmates in a space of roughly twenty-five feet wide by some twenty feet long and boxed in between the deck and deck-head barely ten feet above. Secured to the deck-head were all sorts of piping, electrical cables and mechanical control rods. Most vessels would not have enough space for all the ratings to sling their hammocks and so a number would sleep on the benches or seat lockers located along the ship's side. Some even had to sleep on the deck.

During rough weather, which was most of the time in the North

Atlantic, these small ships would plunge their bows deep down to the level of the forecastle deck, then the wave would recede leaving the forward end completely suspended in air. This pitching motion was also accompanied by tossing and rolling. The forces exerted by these seas on the hull, the sides of which were barely a quarter of an inch thick, caused plates to fracture and leak with the result that the ratings' mess decks, especially those up forward, were frequently awash in sea water up to six inches deep, sloshing back and forth across the mess deck. These conditions made it impossible for anybody to sleep on the deck and even those sleeping on the side lockers were soaked as the water surged across the deck, splashing upwards against the lockers. This environment caused a high incidence of tuberculosis among naval ratings.

Knowing all this, Ted felt morally obliged to share the truth with these starry-eyed, patriotic boys and young men, but decided against clouding their dreams. The Allies needed these young sailors and, regrettably, they would just have to experience their fate.

The three spent the night on HMS *York* and next morning they were given the name and address of a private home in a part of the city called Sunnyside. They were to take up residence there and to phone Naval Headquarters next morning after settling in. The mystery of ALG/C1 deepened.

Chapter 10

Mystery of ALG/C1, Solved

Their landlady was a war-widow of Irish descent with three teenaged daughters. The artificers were made to feel at home and the landlady was obviously thankful for the lodging allowance the Navy were paying her.

Next morning after a good night's sleep and a plentiful Canadian breakfast, they phoned the Navy and were told a car would be sent to pick them up. The car drove south, then east alongside the lake. Ploughs were clearing the overnight accumulation of snow, causing traffic to slow down and back up. Peering out of the car window, Ted noticed the road was appropriately named Lakeshore Boulevard. He recognised Union Station as they passed, just before they reached what appeared to be large grain-storage silos with the name 'Canadian Maple Leaf Mills' painted in large white letters across the front. The car turned right through some gates and into a badly-surfaced waterfront area occupied by low-lying office, warehouse and workshop buildings.

The trio got out of the car at an office building and were directed to an upstairs office. As they entered, a Royal Navy Engineer Commander arose from his desk and greeted them with a cheerful, 'Welcome aboard.'

The complex was obviously a shipyard. Ted caught a glimpse of two small hulls propped up on slipways at the water's edge as he looked out of the office window.

With a little sarcastic grin on his face the officer asked if they had had a pleasant trip. 'Not bad,' answered all three together in a half-hearted manner. The officer then explained that the trio would become part of a grand-sounding organisation, known as the 'British Admiralty Technical Mission'. Ted thought to himself, 'This still doesn't explain the mysterious code: ALG/C1.'

The shipyard had been given the task to build a number of British-designed minesweeping vessels. They were to be the largest and most versatile of this type of ship. Not only would they be capable of performing the standard naval wire sweep, known as the Oropesa, they would also be capable of destroying both magnetic and acoustic mines. Another improvement in the design was a feature to cut down on the loss of life in the event of being struck by a mine. The seamen and petty officers, besides having a mess forward and below the main deck, had another mess further aft and on the main deck. This mess they would occupy during minesweeping operations, the water-tight hatches and doors to the forward mess being closed. The fleet sweepers were also fitted with weapons, radar and submarine detection equipment which made them valuable as escort and anti-submarine vessels.

The artificers were to stand by the building of their vessel and to join her on becoming operational. They were given an office one floor above one of the machine shops. In it they studied the plans of the ship and got to know every nook and cranny, deck, ladder, hatch, pipe, fire hydrant, valve and piece of machinery from stem to stern of the vessel. It was all part of the training drummed into Ted: 'Know Your Ship.'

This new class of Fleet minesweeper came to be known as the Algerine class, this being the name given to the first to be built. So that was the secret of the draft-chit code. ALG for Algerine, C for Canada and 1 probably for the first to be built. So much for Ted's Algiers and the Casbah fantasy.

Chapter 11

Building a Minesweeper

Their ship was to be named *Aries*. After a spell in their shipyard office, they would wander through the machine, plating and welding shops, checking on the various components that would come together in the 'sweeper'. Then they would wander aboard the ship to watch progress and take note of any mistake: bad welding, defective items or materials. Their day would end at 4 p.m. and with a wash and brush-up they were all set for ashore in Toronto.

Standing outside the shipyard gates with their thumbs pointing up the road, it was only a matter of time before they were picked up and taken to wherever they requested. Toronto really appreciated servicemen. The three generally headed for the bar of the hotel close to their digs, since most places stopped serving beer after 6 p.m. They made sure a goodly area of the table was well-stocked before the deadline. They could then lie back and relax until they felt it was time to head for the digs and dinner.

For the first few weeks they preferred to spend their evenings in the warm digs listening to the news from the home front and playing cards. The weather was still bitterly cold and their clothing totally inadequate for any lengthy excursions outdoors. It was bad enough to walk each morning down to the Lakeshore Boulevard and thumb a lift to the shipyard. Invariably they would be picked up within seconds, but during that period they would stamp their feet rapidly and thrust their noses under their coats to draw whatever warm air there was from their bodies.

At the location where they generally assembled for their morning ride, three or four enclosed trucks would be backed up by the lake shore whilst the drivers ventured out onto the frozen lake with saws with which they would cut large one foot thick blocks of ice from the surface of the freshwater lake. The blocks were then transported to large Swiss-cottage-like structures made entirely of horizontally-laid tree trunks. The ice would be stacked inside and completely packed in tight with a thick blanket of insulating sawdust. During the hot summer months, the ice would be unpacked and sold for use in the city's ice-boxes.

Although ice still lay thick on the lake and people were walking on it between the mainland and Centre Island way out in the harbour, an area of free water was kept open along the shipyard's building berths. In early April 1943 the three artificers witnessed their first sideways launching. The hull barely moved at first as it was coaxed by the launching crew. Then gradually it picked up momentum and finally it tore down the slips as though anxious to be embraced by its natural element. The entire starboard side of the vessel hit the water with a loud smack and splash and the tremendous amount of displaced water rose up to the upper deck. The vessel stopped momentarily and slowly rolled over to port. Eventually after two or three ever-decreasing rolls to port and starboard, the sweeper, now on an even keel, moved slowly out from shore whereupon steadying lines, one from the bows and the other from the stern, were secured to the two attending tugs.

The vessel was now under control. However, the shore staff noticed that she appeared to be settling down in the water. Sure enough, she was taking on water. Fortunately she had a number of salvage pumps on board. These were brought into play and managed to stem the ingress of water until the vessel was dry-docked and the sources of the flooding repaired. This incident and numerous others prompted much more detailed quality control inspection by the Navy and shipyard management.

Inwardly, Ted was not surprised by the level of workmanship and skills. After all, Canada had been primarily an agricultural country up to the beginning of the war, being referred to as the 'breadbasket of the world'. The war changed that as Canada and the United States became the

'Arsenals of Democracy'. Thousands of unskilled men and women moved from the farms and small communities all across Canada to the newly developing industrial and manufacturing centres in the major cities. They came not only for patriotic reasons, but for well-paying jobs and the city lights. Toronto Shipbuilding Company, formed in 1941, was one of these wartime industries put together to build ships for the United States, British and Canadian Navies. Apart from the fact that Canada as a whole had a very limited shipbuilding industry, most of the workers flocking to the Toronto Shipbuilding Company had never been aboard or even seen a real ship.

The unskilled workers started off as assistant labourers; after six weeks and having proved themselves, they could become labourers. The yard ran a full-time training scheme where labourers showing the right type of potential could apply to be trained in a number of semi-skilled jobs, such as a screwing-machine operator, riveter, blacksmith's assistant, plumber's assistant or drilling machine operator. Others could take the prolonged welder's course.

To increase productivity, piece work was introduced. It turned out to be a mixed blessing, for in some operations like welding, though many more linear feet of welding were completed during a shift, the quality in many cases suffered. Sometimes, fortunately, the defects were found and corrected before the vessels left the yard. However in many cases, unfortunately, the poor workmanship manifested itself halfway across the Atlantic during bad weather. The skilled labour force required less supervision and their standard gradually improved as they became familiar with shipyard and marine engineering practice.

The yard's purchasing department sometimes went a little haywire as Ted remembered the agent who mistakenly ordered thousands of dollars worth of bronze valves and other fittings. They should have been cast iron. In a panic lest his mistake should be discovered, the agent loaded them onto a barge and dumped them in the middle of Lake Ontario.

Taking all things into consideration, this shipyard on the shores of Lake Ontario and its personnel rendered a great service to the Allied cause.

Chapter 12

Money Problems

Towards late spring, the trio changed digs and moved into a large-framed house on King Street, one of the main east-to-west-running thoroughfares in Toronto. They were given the large living room on the ground floor facing King Street. Beside the landlord, his wife and his daughter there were at least thirteen lodgers beside the three artificers. One was an officer in the Canadian Navy, two men belonged to the Canadian Broadcasting Corporation and yet another man was a manager at the John Inglis factory. The remaining eight were young female secretaries, bank tellers and shop assistants.

Breakfast and dinner times were quite a scene, for in the dining room was a long wide table at which all sixteen lodgers would be seated, that is, eight on either side. The landlady would sit at the head and her daughter at the other end. Ted never saw the landlord and presumed he was supervising in the kitchen. All during the meals, two maids would constantly fly back and forth between the great swinging doors of the kitchen and the table. The weather was becoming warmer and the trio found their walk down to the lake shore and their ride to the shipyard a great deal more pleasant.

Their main concern at this time was money. They all allotted money home and they were finding the Canadian cost of living high. They were becoming down at the heel. They had approached the authorities about an overseas cost of living allowance, but realised the wheels of the Admiralty grind very slowly.

They would get a job. Ted and George scanned the newspapers and answered an advertisement for help at Loblaw, the giant supermarket. They appeared at the company's main warehouse on Spadina Avenue, not far from the shipyard. They were interviewed by the manager who happened to have come from Sunderland (not far from George's and Ted's home town) many years ago. After some pleasant reminiscing, he took the pair to the loading ramps. Their job was to load the large tractor-trailers with merchandise for the company's supermarkets all over Southern Ontario. They were to clock-in at eight o'clock each evening and work through until four next morning.

Amongst the merchandise was wonderful fresh fruit of every description from all over Canada and the States: strawberries, raspberries, blackcurrants, mangoes, peaches, apricots, bananas and much much more. It was like being in Covent Garden before the war. The temptation was too great. 'Nobody will miss a few strawberries here and a couple of bananas there,' they tried to convince themselves and so their appetites grew. This was great: getting paid and feeding on the healthiest of foods.

After a week, the manager called them into his office. 'Now lads!' he said, 'I've been getting complaints from our branch stores that stuff is arriving short in quantity and weight. I know you need the money so I'll give you another chance. Don't let it happen again!'

Rather sheepishly the two sauntered out of the office. For over two weeks they resisted the temptation to taste of the forbidden fruit as they loaded the trucks and unloaded the railway freight cars. Some-times the freight cars came in loaded with cubic cardboard boxes measuring three feet per side. They were full of matches. Occasionally a box would land on its corners as it was heaved from the freight car onto the concrete loading ramp. The energy of the impact would ignite the matches in one terrific explosion and send a sheet of flame leaping towards the ceiling. At first it seemed like great fun for the pair, until they came to the sober realisation that the freight car and probably many more could go up in flames and perhaps take the whole warehouse with them.

Fruit started to go missing again. This time the manager removed them from the Garden of Eden and put them in the garage to wash the company's mud-laden trucks.

The fun of suddenly confronting each other with powerful jets of ice-cold water soon wore thin, especially after getting back to the digs at five o'clock in the morning soaked to the skin. Suddenly, at one o'clock one morning, Ted gave George a thorough soaking with his hose and yelled, 'That's it, I quit!' and walked off, punched his card and made for the digs.

Chick in the meantime had, through one of the Canadian Broadcasting executives at the digs, managed to get a half hour slot singing on the Canadian Broadcasting Corporation network twice a week. The show was called 'Chick Henderson Sings'. It was a huge success and money began to pour in for him.

Sometimes Ted would accompany Chick to the broadcasting studio. He admired the casual way Chick readied himself for the broadcast. With his right hand cupped behind his right ear, he would step up to the microphone and commence right on cue.

At times Ted would listen to the broadcast at the digs. On those occasions the large dining room table had been cleared and the radio placed in the centre. All the girls including the landlady and her daughter would gather round awaiting the announcer to say, 'Ladies and Gentlemen; Chick Henderson Sings!'

At the first sound of Chick's voice the whole female assembly would let out one great scream. It reminded Ted of the ear-shattering yell that went up from New York's bobby-sockers when Frank Sinatra gave forth. It amazed Ted to observe that these girls, having the choice to listen to Chick or to Sinatra broadcasting from New York, preferred to listen to Chick. On one occasion Chick and Ted were listening to Sinatra broadcasting from New York, then after one song Chick made a remark Ted never forgot. He simply said after a quiet moment of reflection, 'That fella's going a long way!'

Money started piling up for Chick. He got fitted out with a beautifully-tailored doe-skin uniform and civilian clothes, and bought the most expensive gifts for his wife and small daughter.

Ted and George, either through envy or jealousy, started to think seriously about making money. That meant a job.

Chapter 13

Half a Day for King George, Half a Day for King Self

This time Ted wanted a well-paid job. After some thought he said to himself, 'Why not the shipyard?'

The shipyard it was. George joined him. They were handed a large white pin-on button with their employee number and department stamped on and signed on as night-shift fitters. Each day just before 4 p.m. they changed out of uniform and into a pair of coveralls, placed a striped locomotive-engineer's peaked cap on their heads, dashed downstairs and clocked-in for work.

For Ted promotion was rapid. Within two weeks he was assistant foreman and he was full foreman after another three. During his first week as assistant foreman, one of the sweepers had experienced an overheated main bearing during trials. He was given the job to investigate. About midnight an Engineer Commander bent down over Ted as he was working on the bearing. 'What seems to be the trouble?' the Commander said in his pukka Royal Navy accent.

Ted, trying to hide his face and his voice, pulled his locomotive engineer's cap down as far as he could, and, summoning up as good a Canadian accent as possible, replied, 'Dirt had blocked the lubricating-oil holes and other dirt had penetrated the side of the bearing causing scoring of the white metal and shaft journal.' Then he continued, 'After we've cleaned everything up and scraped away the high spots, the bearing will be fine and ready to go.'

'Well done!' bellowed the Commander.

Ted wanted to end the conversation as quickly as possible before the officer recognised him. However he thought now was a good opportunity to make a point that had been troubling him. So, burying his head further down into the bearing, he mumbled, 'Sir, I suggest that we will continue to have these bearing problems if action isn't taken to protect these engines from the weather as they stand in the yard protected only by the flimsiest of tarpaulins where in the winter snow piles up and blows into the end bearings. In summer, it's sand and other abrasives that does the same thing.' The Commander gave a cough and promised he'd look into it. With that he yelled, 'Good show, carry on!'

With that Ted breathed a sigh of relief as he watched the gold braid disappear up the engine room ladder. He stood up from the crouching position to relieve his aching muscles and in doing so displaced a 500 watt lamp which crashed down and smashed. Bending his arm under the shade he was feeling round blindly to remove the broken bulb when in an instant his entire body was propelled across the engine room. The whole length of his back made contact with the curved contour of the ship's side and he slithered down into the bilges. His hand had short-circuited the electrodes of the broken bulb. With his heart thumping like a sledge hammer, it took him a full ten minutes to realise what had happened. He'd had experiences where electricity had prevented his fingers from letting go of a live wire, but this was the first time he'd been thrown.

The Commander was as good as his word. Management moved all engines under permanent cover and all main bearings were opened up and inspected before any vessel proceeded on trials.

As foreman, Ted was allotted an office from which he detailed the members of his gang with their night-shift jobs. George was one of his outside fitters: that is, George's place of work was aboard the ships and not in the shops. Ted sensed a little resentment or even jealousy in George's behaviour as George was assigned his nightly task.

One night George was given a relatively simple task, a task that he would normally have taken, sized up and completed to Ted's satisfaction. This time he demanded to be given full instructions on how to go about the job. The task was that he make up two sets of boiler firing tool holders for each of three ships and finally install them on the boiler fronts. He knew there were no drawings for these items but still he demanded them before he could start work. Sensing the stonewalling tactics, Ted took him to one side and asked him to sit down. He then proceeded to go through each operation step by step. First of all you go aboard ship no.35 and take notes about the item already installed aboard her, then you go in the piping shop and get the appropriate number and lengths of pipe cut, thence to the plate shop to get the required blanks burnt out, then to the welding shop to have the blanks welded to the bottom of the pipes, on to the blacksmith's where you'll have two straps made to go round each pipe, then you have the whole assembly transported to each ship, call the welder and have him or her weld the finished article to the boiler fronts.

With a sarcastic grin, George gave Ted an exaggerated salute, yelled, 'Aye, Aye, Sir!' winked at Ted's assistant foreman, turned and disappeared through the door and into the night.

Toward the end of the shift Ted, doing his nightly rounds, found that George had indeed completed his task satisfactorily and with time to spare. George was entertaining his girlfriend Rosie, the welder, on the upper deck of one of the ships.

Chapter 14

George Lives It Up

With money in his pocket to spare and his equally prosperous girlfriend, Rosie, George and she would turn every Saturday into a night on the town. Occasionally on Saturday night Chick and Ted would be returning to the digs on King Street when their street car would stop amidst a flurry of raised voices. They could hear George's voice giving forth with his favourite and only tune, 'Ave, Maria'. If time was on their side, Ted and Chick would exit from the front door and escape. Other times their only way to remain undetected was to take off their caps and sink away down into their seats.

George would spend most Saturday nights as a guest of the Toronto Police, having been taken in for carrying an open 26-ounce bottle of Johnnie Walker Black Label whisky protruding from his coat pocket. On Sunday morning Chick and Ted would go down to police headquarters and vouch for him. The police would release George into their custody, but more importantly the bottle of whisky was turned over to the pair. Toronto was dry on Sundays and so they spent Sunday afternoon drinking to George's health.

George's feelings of envy were not solely against Ted. In the back of his mind, whether it was true or not, he thought Chick was having an affair with the landlady's daughter and even with the landlady herself. His envy of Chick's amorous flirtations whether real or not manifested themselves one evening when Chick and Ted entering their bed-sitting room found the lampshades, bed headboards, potted plants and ornaments festooned with limp, soggy and dripping condoms. George was sitting relaxed in the armchair with a contented grin on his face. Chick and Ted played along with his practical signs of debauchery, but inwardly they realised the evidence pointed to a poorly-staged hoax.

Chapter 15

Our American Cousins

George in a letter from home found out he had an aunt living in Detroit and decided he would like to see her. Ted suggested he put in for some leave, George said he didn't want to go alone and asked Ted if he would accompany him. They both put in for leave and got seven days.

Next day, they removed the contents from their khaki-coloured gas-mask bags and replaced them with a toothbrush, paste, soap, razor, face flannel, towel and a brush and comb. They walked down to Lake Shore Boulevard and stood by the side of the road with their thumbs pointing toward the west. Within minutes they were picked up by a truck. The driver told them he was only going as far as Niagara Falls. 'That's fine!' replied the travellers.

They arrived at the Falls about noon and spent almost two hours admiring the magnificent scene and sensing with awe the mighty force of millions of gallons per minute crashing down into the chasm below. The whole experience was uplifting; even the air seemed to give them a feeling of well-being.

They crossed into the United States over the Rainbow Bridge. They showed their papers to the Customs and Immigration authorities and were given the 'Welcome' treatment. A young married couple gave them a lift as far as Buffalo and invited them for cocktails at one of the large downtown hotels. The drinks and hors d'oeuvres hit the spot. It was early evening and still light when they eventually said 'Goodbye' to the young couple.

They walked for miles through Buffalo seeking out the main road west. Finally at dusk they hit what was obviously the major six-lane highway heading westwards. Truck after truck, trailer after trailer, tanker after tanker roared past the sailors. Clouds of dust and paper were swept up and chased behind the never-ending traffic. It looked as though the whole of America was on that one stretch of road. The two felt as though they were putting their lives on the line by approaching too close to it. Eventually, pulling their caps well down over their heads and half closing their eyes against the clouds of dust, they approached as near the edge of the road as possible and stuck up their thumbs.

A truck almost the length of a city block gave a blast like a ship's siren on its horn and with squealing, smoking brakes, pulled smartly off to the side of the road. The sailors had to run for about a hundred yards before coming abreast of the truck. 'Get in!' yelled the heavy plaid-shirted driver. Getting in wasn't quite that simple. One artificer had to climb up a three-runged ladder behind the other and into a cavernous cab.

Once the pair were aboard the driver stretched out his arm and pulled the door closed with a lever.

'Where ya bound for, guys?' yelled the driver above the roaring engine.

'Detroit,' shouted the artificers. 'I'll take you as far as Erie,' shouted the driver.

'Thanks,' was the quick reply.

Ted didn't care to yell his throat sore in trying to overcome the pulsating roar in the cab and yet out of common courtesy he knew he had to answer the driver's questions. 'Thank God,' he thought as the driver limited himself to very few.

'Where ya from?'

'England,' shouted the pair.

'I guess our boys are showing you a thing or two over there,' he yelled with a self-important grin on his face.

Ted had heard this very same remark by Yanks several times and voiced his reply according to the circumstances. In this case the driver was serving the pair's purpose, so Ted replied with a short, 'I guess so.'

Stretching behind the trio was a wide comfortable-looking bed stretching the full width of the cab.

'Where you boys figuring on sleeping tonight?' shouted the trucker.

'Don't know,' yelled Ted.

'There's a truckers' stopover just the other side of Erie, that's where I'm kipping!' he went on.

'Will they take us?' asked Ted.

'Sure thing!' was the reply.

'What do you say, George?'

'OK with me!'

It was almost midnight when the huge rig pulled into the stopover. The whole area was packed with these motorised monsters. Inside the layover the cigarette and cigar smoke was thick, the jukebox was belting out Lena Horne's 'Stormy Weather' and the truck drivers were conversing and laughing with the waitresses.

As the three made their way toward an empty table, the truck driver, still yelling, asked, 'What ya going to have, guys?'

'No, that's all right, we'll pay for our own stuff!'

'The hell you will, it's not every day I gits to treat the British Navy!'

'OK,' said Ted, 'we appreciate it.'

As they ended the meal and sleep started to creep up on Ted, he looked round at the dozens of truckers and imagined a similar scene portrayed in Steinbeck's *Grapes of Wrath* where a similar breed of truckers had helped out Tom Hoad's family of Okies and always left a good tip for the help behind the counters of the roadside diners.

The pair slept well into the morning. At breakfast the waitress serving them told them that Joe (their driver) had left early and left her with a message to say, 'Goodbye to the sailors,' for him. After a good wash and shave the pair felt fit and with a fond 'Cheerio' to all the waitresses, they headed out of the parking area and onto the main highway. No sooner had they selected their next 'picking-up' site than a giant truck slowly pulled out of the stopover parking area and pulled up beside them.

'Where you going, Jack?' enquired the rosy-faced driver.

'Detroit,' they replied.

'Sorry, I'm only going as far as Cleveland.'

'How far is that?' asked Ted.

'Oh, about 130 miles I dare say,' responded the trucker.

'OK, thanks,' said Ted as he and George mounted the rig.

The superhighway skirted Lake Erie most of the way. The lake looked beautiful and calm in the morning sunlight. George mentioned how smooth the stretch of water was.

'It's not always like that,' responded the driver. 'No!' he continued, 'that there lake can be one hell of a bitch when she gits roused. In fact she's the most dangerous of all five Great Lakes and there's many a good ship been lost out there!'

'I wonder why that is,' interjected Ted.

'Some guy told me it's because it's so shallow that the waves git sharp and choppy when the wind blows hard!' replied the trucker.

The driver reached forward and turned the radio on. 'There ya go, the kid from Hoboken,' he yelled. It was Frank Sinatra singing.

'We've got a buddy by the name of Chick Henderson way back at our digs in Toronto could teach that Hoboken fella a thing or two!' barked up George.

'Is that so?' said the trucker, looking at Ted for reassurance.

They began running through the suburbs of Cleveland just after 1 p.m. The trucker announced he had to make a delivery to the GM (General Motors) works and asked where the pair wanted to be let off.

'Anywhere,' Ted said, then added, 'the GM works will do!'

The works was a massive complex and as the truck backed up to an unloading deck, Ted could see what he thought was a crowd of men in naval uniforms way up ahead. Shaking hands and thanking the driver, the pair climbed down from the truck's cab. Being curious, Ted approached the crowd of uniformed men.

'Hells bells,' he suddenly exclaimed. 'It's a bloody great bunch of Royal Navy artificers!'

'Jesus Christ, it's like bloody Chatham Barracks!' yelled out George in disbelief.

As they approached the crowd, Ted could see that he and George were receiving a critical eye from the older artificers. No doubt the rumpled and dust-laden condition of the pair's uniforms was under scrutiny. Recognising a Chatham tiffy, Ted asked what was going on. It turned out that they and many more had been sent to Cleveland to become experts on the running and maintenance of GM diesel engines which were to propel all types of landing craft. Nobody suggested why so many were receiving instructions, but it didn't take Ted long to realise that preparations must already be underway for the invasion of Europe.

One of the artificers told Ted that GM was putting on a big dance for the Royal Navy that night and suggested that Ted and George might as well take advantage. Taking George to one side, Ted suggested that with their scruffy uniforms they would stick out like a sore thumb at the dance.

'Are you crazy?' retorted George. 'I'm not going to miss out on all that booze!'

'I'm sorry, but I'm off!' said Ted. 'And besides,' he continued, 'we're no novelty here amongst this crowd. Let's push on to Detroit.'

Reluctantly George gave in and after a bite to eat in the cafeteria courtesy of GM, they moved through Cleveland to the western suburbs.

Once again an obliging trucker picked them up and once again they settled back into the cab's deep seat. This time the trailer was heading for Chicago; however, the driver said he would drop them off in Toledo, some 120 miles west of Cleveland. The trucker asked them the usual questions: 'Where are you from?' and 'How's the war going over there?' and 'I guess our boys are showing you a thing or two over there!' Ted smiled at George.

Every so many miles there would be billboards with a large Uncle Sam asking everybody to 'Buy War Bonds until it hurts!' Many houses had a white silk flag surrounded by gold lace and with a blue star in the centre hanging in the front window, signifying one member of the family was serving in the armed forces. Some houses had two, three and even four stars in the flag indicating that the father and three sons or all four sons were away serving Uncle Sam.

At Toledo the pair said 'Goodbye' and 'Thank you' to the Chicago-bound trucker, and, feeling a little tired, they sat down on a bench and watched the evening rush hour traffic. Across the road was a bus depot with a massive sign in bright winking white lights, flashing out its message: 'Let Greyhound do the Driving.'

Suddenly in a pensive mood, Ted mumbled, 'Why not!'

'What yer mean?' asked George.

'To hell with the trucks!' said Ted. 'Let's ride into Detroit in comfort. Let's take the bus!'

The bus arrived in downtown Detroit at about 8 p.m. Now they had to find George's aunt's place. The taxi man knew the street.

Ted stood back as George knocked on the door. They could hear a woman's voice screaming, 'All right, I'm coming, I'm coming.'

The door was opened by a slight wizen-faced woman.

'Yes, what do you want?' she screamed as she looked the artificers up and down.

'Aunt Lizzie?' George said in an inquiring manner. Ted was beginning to think they'd got the wrong house and hoped they hadn't got the wrong city.

'Who are you?' she demanded, half closing the door.

'I'm ya sister Gertie's bairn, Georgie!'

Her tense eyes relaxed a little and took on a searching look.

'What yer doing here?' she enquired. Ted felt a little more relieved. The woman had definitely kept a little of her north country accent.

George told her he was in the British Navy and was standing-by a ship in Canada and that his Ma told him to look up his Aunt Lizzie when he got to America.

'Weel, I'll be blessed!' she said, opening the door wide. 'Cum'mon in!' Charging down the passage in front of them, she yelled, 'Tom, ye'll never believe it, its wor lassie's lad Georgie from Darlington!'

Tom was definitely not from Darlington, Ted thought, on hearing his voice. He was obviously Irish.

And so George, his aunt and uncle went on reminiscing well into the night.

Ted was relieved when Aunt Lizzie called them to the table to eat. He asked if there was any place handy where he could get his uniform cleaned and pressed and shirt washed.

56

'Sure thing,' said Tom. 'There's an all night joint just round the corner. I'll pop down with them now and you can get them back first thing in the morning.'

Aunt Lizzie suggested they eat first, then Ted could have a shower and give his uniform and whatever else needed cleaning to Tom, whilst Ted turned in.

'Good idea!' exclaimed Ted.

George, Aunt Lizzie and her husband went on talking into the wee hours of the morning.

The shower was so therapeutic and the air-conditioned bedroom oh so comfortable. Ted soon dropped off into a deep rejuvenating sleep. Next morning the tiffies awoke to the smell of percolating coffee and toast.

Aunt Lizzie did them well. The breakfast table had a variety of cereals, marmalades, jams, jellies, jugs of orange, fresh butter, doughnuts and milk. As soon as George and Ted were seated she brought in a plate of fried eggs, ham and bacon, then a plate full of waffles along with corn and maple syrup. In the centre of the table was a large basket full of fresh, juicy, golden peaches from Aunt Lizzie's garden.

Tom had already left for work before the pair arose. He worked just down the end of the street at the Ford Motor Works in Dearborn. After more reminiscing between George and his aunt, the artificers took their leave, saying they were off to explore downtown Detroit.

Once outside and rounding the corner at the bottom of the street, they could see the massive buildings of the Ford complex stretching for what seemed like miles in both directions. There were also tall chimney stacks belching out smoke, some black, some white. The whole area within the wire fences was a hive of activity. It struck Ted that wartime employment in the States must be close to a hundred per cent and the average worker's wages must be at an all time high.

The shops downtown were full of good quality goods and reasonably cheap by Canadian standards. Good restaurants offering a large variety of national and foreign foods abounded. The bars of the better class hotels were well furnished and comfortable and the shelves stocked with every brand of Scotch whisky, some brands that Ted had never seen at home even before the war. Every brand of cigarette and cigar was available and on the counter there was always a plentiful supply of all sorts of snacks and hors d'oeuvres.

American servicemen were everywhere. The GIs had such good-looking and well-tailored uniforms that Ted had a job distinguishing between them and their officers. All the servicemen were well-disposed towards Ted and George once they found out that the pair were members of the British Navy and insisted on buying the drinks. A number of servicemen wore four and five medal ribbons. Ted asked what campaign they were for and was surprised to learn that some were for good workmanship and that some of the lads hadn't as yet been overseas.

That evening George's aunt and uncle took the pair out to dinner to a cosy little Italian restaurant. The food was excellent. The place had a Neapolitan motif with a small band seated in one corner. As the evening wore on and the customers became more mellow, a Caruso-like figure drifted from table to table lulling them into sentimental thoughts of mama or lost loves. During the meal, Tom announced that he had managed to arrange a guided tour of the Ford works for George and Ted.

Next morning Tom met the pair at the main gate security office and conducted them to the visitors' room. There the artificers were given a hard hat, a pair of safety glasses and a large red button on which in white letters was the word 'visitor'.

After signing the visitors' book and pinning the button on their lapel, their guide leading the way asked them to follow. They were shown the full operation of the manufacturing process, right from the delivery of the raw materials to the finished products ready for dispatch to sales outlets.

The tour took over three hours to complete. During the visit to the engine-testing facility, the artificers spent some time in the laboratory amid the loud pulsating din of several engines on the test beds, after which they were led through thick, heavy and insulated doors into the control room. With the doors slammed shut all lab noise suddenly ceased. The control room was lined from wall to wall with all sorts of gauges, manometers, recorders, flow-meters and switches and on the benches in front of the shatter-proof observation windows were row upon row of levers, knobs and coloured indicator lights. Presently a man in a white lab coat and with a set of earmuffs sprung around his neck approached the pair.

'Good afternoon,' he said, shaking Ted's hand and then George's. 'I'm Ron Birch,' he went on. 'Which part of the UK do you come from?'

He then went on to say he was from Dagenham. Ted jumped in with, 'I know it well. I studied for my National Certificate in Mechanical Engineering at the South-East Essex Technical College!'

'Well, I'll be buggered!' Ron responded excitedly, 'so did I. I took my Ordinary and Higher Nationals there!'

Ted recalled that he himself had been one of the first students to attend the college when it opened in 1937 and he also remembered that all the engineering apprentices at Ford's Dagenham works had had to attend day and evening courses at the college. In fact Ford had provided about eighty per cent of the student body.

'So what are you doing now?' asked Ted.

'Oh!' replied Ron, 'this is my present domain. I'm in charge of the engine testing laboratory.'

Ted was feeling a little uncomfortable for George's sake. He and Ron were monopolising the conversation. On second thoughts, it was now his turn to reminisce. The guide was becoming a little impatient, and Ted mentioned that they had a lot more to see. Ron got the hint. They finally parted after Ron had handed over the address of his parents in Dagenham with the hope that Ted might drop in on them one day and relate the story of meeting their son.

It was late afternoon before George and Ted finally made their exit through the main gate. Though tiring, the experience had been a real revelation of Yankee 'know how' to Ted. From beginning to end the whole manufacturing process had been planned in the most precise manner; material was moved from one spot to the next by machines with the minimum of manual labour. Each part arrived on time for the next operation and as components were used the storage bins were refilled immediately. If a tool became worn it was immediately thrown out and replaced with a new one. There was little or no loss motion on the part of the workers. Chargemen constantly patrolled the assembly lines to forestall any potential problem that might interfere with the smooth manufacturing operation.

Should a worker experience a problem or become sick, he or his immediate neighbour would signal the charge hand and a worker on a less essential job would be sent in as a relief. All working areas were constantly kept clean and no object was allowed to occupy any clearly marked area for the exclusive use of wheeled vehicles. There were even duplicate assembly lines so that on regular maintenance periods, one line could be shut down for preventative maintenance whilst the second line continued to operate. The complex was self-sufficient as regards power with enough emergency power units to cope with any major outage.

The workers during this period were well-satisfied, for they were amongst the highest paid in the States. If only Toronto Shipbuilding Company could be torn down and a new yard built with similar planning ideas and the appropriate machinery installed along the lines of the Ford yard, Ted thought, they could be sending ships to sea in a matter of weeks, not months. Unfortunately such a transformation would take many months and many millions of dollars and who knows, the war could be over by then.

Ted and George's time in Detroit flew past so swiftly that Saturday came soon and in order to get back to Toronto and the Navy, they figured they'd have to leave Detroit on Sunday night. Aunt Lizzie had already suggested that she and Tom would drive them across the river to Windsor, Ontario and they could take the train right into Toronto.

It was Saturday; the two were determined to enjoy their last full day in the city. Having taken a shower, shaved and put on a clean shirt and collar and a newly-cleaned and pressed uniform, they made their way uptown to the bright lights.

On the way, George suddenly remarked, 'I'm thirsty, let's drop in here for a quick one.'

'Here' happened to be a dingy little drinking hole named Paddy's Pub. Once inside and seated at the bar, Ted knew at once they had made the wrong choice. There was a picture of Mr De Valera behind the bar, the frame of which was draped in black cloth. Small flags of the Irish Republic were planted in several glasses and vases amongst the liquor bottles on the back shelf and across one wall above the exit door was a black banner with large white letters sewn on, spelling out 'IRA, All the Way!'

The bar-tender in off-handed manner asked, 'What's it to be?' in an unmistakable Irish accent.

George said, 'Guinness.'

'I'll take the same,' said Ted feeling more like getting as far away from the place as possible and cursing the Guinness for delaying his departure.

'Where yer fram?' quizzed the man behind the bar. The question was totally unnecessary unless he wanted to make sure that all his customers heard the answer. Anyway his question was answered before Ted could respond by a group of scruffy-looking characters sitting at a table in the corner of the room.

'What ya limeys doing drinking good Irish stout?'

George and Ted pretended they hadn't heard the comment, then purposely took their time drinking the stout. Ted hated every gulp of the stuff. Taking a calculated risk Ted asked George if he wanted another, giving a great sigh of relief when George said, 'No!' They sauntered slowly toward the door and out into the evening without saying a word.

After walking a few yards across an open area of sparse grass, soil and stones, Ted felt a terrific blow to the back of his head. The force sent him flying forward and flat on his face. Rolling on to his back and looking up he recognised four of the hooligans from the pub. Getting to his feet, he thought, 'Oh, my nice clean uniform!' Quickly though he forgot about his uniform. This quartet meant business, so, striking whoever came within reach, he tried to ward off the avalanche of blows coming from all quarters. After a few minutes he realised that he had to protect his back so he edged toward the wall of the pub and placed his back against it.

Why wasn't George coming to his assistance, he thought. For a moment among the flaying limbs he caught sight of George standing back out of reach, intently following the fight and with a slight grin on his face. Was he in collusion with the Irish thugs, thought Ted, or too stupid to realise the plight that Ted was in? It became apparent to Ted that he was about to become a sacrificial Englishman for the havoc that King William of Orange and the rest of his race had brought on Catholic Ireland. These four Irish-Americans had obviously built up a hatred for the likes of Ted ever since they could understand what their parents, grandparents and great-grandparents had taught them. They probably saw themselves as an extension of the IRA in America.

In the meantime Ted was on the ground being savagely kicked in every part of his anatomy, only managing to regain his feet by clawing the wall. He shouted, 'Play the game. I'll take you on one at a time.'

The appeal whipped them up into further fury as they intensified their attack. In a desperate last ditch stand, Ted stood up, bleeding profusely from head, nose and mouth wounds, and yelled to George, 'These bastards don't believe in the Marquess of Queensberry rules!'

Whether the mention of the Marquis brought back memories of his boxing heydeys, Ted never found out, but instantly George put his head down and came charging into the melee like a raging bull. Blow after blow like the kick from a mule landed on the face of each and every Irishman as he sent them reeling. The scene was like a tonic for Ted and, ignoring his injuries, he revelled in getting some good solid punches in before the quartet broke off the fight one by one and disappeared into an alleyway between some buildings. Ted was never able to find out why George left it until it was almost too late to come to his shipmate's rescue. Was he jealous of the younger and more senior man or was it because Ted was now a shipyard foreman, or did he have a resentment against regular Royal Navy personnel?

Rage was still coursing through George's body and he wanted to go back to the pub and sort out the rest of the unsavoury characters and especially the bar-tender. However Ted persuaded him to leave well alone. They made their way to one of the larger hotels where Ted bought a new shirt and collar in one of the shops in the basement. Then he got the hotel's room service to clean the mud from his uniform and press it. They both washed and brushed up.

Three Tiffies and a Sweeper

Apart from Ted's black eye, cut head, busted lip and limp, they were almost as good as new. It was Saturday night and this was their last night in the US, so they looked and found a good class night-club. The atmosphere inside was gay and cheerful with everybody determined to have a good time. The tiffies pulled themselves up onto a well-upholstered bar stool and ordered a beer and scotch (a boiler maker). Lying back they let go of every tense sinew and relaxed as they slowly sipped their beverage. Ted bought an expensive but good cigar and slowly puffed smoke rings into the air. Discovering it was painful to clamp down on the cigar with the right side of his mouth, he spent the rest of the evening smoking the cigar and drinking through the left side.

A young man in a tuxedo squeezed up to the bar between George and Ted and ordered two drinks. Looking at Ted he said, smiling, 'What happened to you, run into the back of a bus?'

Suddenly Ted felt it hurt even to try to return the smile and he ended up by saying, 'Oh! I ran into some guys who didn't like the look of my face.'

Hearing Ted's accent the young man exclaimed, 'Hi! You're English, aren't you?'

Ted simply said, 'Yes.'

'Have a drink on me; no, better still, I'd like you both to join my wife and friends over at that table,' the young man continued, pointing towards a large table in the centre of the crowded room. Standing by the side of the table, the young man set the two drinks onto the table and announced, 'Folks, I want you to meet these two Brits!' He then introduced the six couples seated round the table by name.

Ted and George nodded in the direction of each and every person seated at the table as their name was announced.

'Waiter!' shouted the young man. 'Please bring two more chairs.' Ted and George were then seated opposite each other, each with somebody's wife or girlfriend on either side. The artificers' every wish was treated as a command as their newly found friends obviously enjoyed the tiffies' company and stories.

After an hour or so a beautiful young lady sitting across the table

63

from Ted made the standard statement, 'I guess our boys are showing you a thing or two over there!'

They were obviously all very patriotic and believed in their boys. Besides they were good company so Ted condescendingly simply said, 'Yes.'

The same young lady was wearing a brooch in the form of the American flag. Ted was fascinated by the way the red, white and blue stones sparkled and flashed under the lights of the night-club. Catching the young woman's eye, Ted complimented her on the beautiful brooch. She took it off and, handing it to Ted, said, 'Here, this is a souvenir from me to you!' Ted wondered if he had sounded like a beggar and said so, but she insisted that she wanted him to have it.

During a period whilst the dance band was taking a rest, a spotlight suddenly lit the table at which the pair were seated. The announcer's voice from the stage suddenly filled the room with, 'Ladies and gentlemen, I want you to give a big hand to two members of the British Navy!' Then, looking towards Ted and George, he said, 'Gentlemen, won't you please stand up.' The whole room broke out into shouts, whistles and clapping.

The announcer then went on to request that the two say something. George gave a quick short, 'Thank you very mooch, it's great to be here!' in an unmistakable north country accent. Ted thought he knew what these people wanted, so he purposely put on a distinctively over-exaggerated Royal Naval Officer's accent. It worked; for the announcer excitedly exclaimed, 'Wow! Just listen to that accent!' The audience were ecstatic and continued to howl, whistle and stamp. Ted noticed that the friends round his table seemed to be lapping up their table's newly-found popularity.

After things had quietened down a little, the announcer requested Ted to 'Give the folks a tune.' In a partial sweat he thought about 'Blaydon Races'. No, that would bugger up his previous well-received accent; besides, who would understand a word of the Geordie song? Then 'There'll always be an England' flashed across his thoughts. Remembering the confrontation earlier in the evening, he immediately dismissed that notion. Then he remembered a song his wife loved and one of which he had got Chick to teach him the words in order that he could surprise his wife next leave. It was 'Stardust Serende'. As he put forth with, 'Beside a garden wall when stars are bright,' the band gently joined in. Ted, who was never normally impressed with his own voice, suddenly felt he had discovered a talent he never knew he had. Maybe a band could turn him into a celebrity.

However badly that Saturday night had begun, it ended above all expectations as far as George and Ted were concerned. As people gradually left the night-club, they would come over and shake hands with the tiffies; most of the women kissed them. Their table hosts lapped up the attention and were the last to vacate the premises.

Aunt Lizzie and her husband were waiting up as the pair returned. George's aunt was shocked when she saw Ted and wanted to hear all the details of the confrontation. She blasted George for ever going anywhere near the neighbourhood of Paddy's Bar; it was the most notorious part of the town and accounted for the majority of murders and major crimes in Detroit.

'How were we to know!' exclaimed Ted, coming to George's defence. By this time she was too involved in cleaning Ted's cuts and abrasions with hydrogen peroxide and covering them up with Band-Aids.

Everybody slept late into Sunday morning. Ted awoke with pains in muscles he never knew he had. It took him ages to get into a standing and walking position. Brunch ended about 3 p.m.

Packing their gas masks didn't take long. Meanwhile George's aunt was packing two large suitcases, each with two gallon jars full of preserved peaches from her garden. She then filled up each suitcase with cans of tomato, orange and apple juice, plus boxes of chocolates, toffees and cookies. In the end she said, 'George, this suitcase is for you. Besides the food I've put in some clothes and other stuff for wor lass, your Mother.' Turning to Ted she said, 'And this case is for you.'

As Ted picked up his case the sheer weight made the sides bulge.

Having packed the suitcases and gas mask bags into the car trunk, all four got into the car and headed for the Canadian National Railway station at Windsor, across the river. Aunt Lizzie, her eyes glistening with tears, kissed the pair goodbye, while Tom gave them a hearty handshake.

The artificers lifted their luggage up and onto luggage racks and then settled back into their seats. They each fell into a deep silence. It didn't take long before George cuddled up in the corner seat and sank into a deep sleep punctuated occasionally by a loud snore which almost caused him to wake. Changing his posture a little he would once again descend into a consuming slumber.

The motion of the train and the rhythmic throb of the wheels on the rails lulled Ted into a pensive mood. He thought of the experiences of the past seven days, of the vitality of the United States and how the war, unlike its devastating effects on his own country, was proving to be beneficial to America in production, employment, high wages and the standard of living. It was true that the States were, like the rest of the Allies, paying dearly with the blood of their men and women in the armed forces. In contrast however this war had penetrated the walls of Ted's fortress island and thousands and thousands of civilians were being killed by the Luftwaffe. It was also true that today, July 1943, there was reason to be optimistic about the outcome of the war. For American and British forces were pushing their way up the boot of Italy and Allied planes had dropped leaflets over Italian cities urging the people to overthrow the Mussolini regime and break their ties with Germany. There was an underlying nagging feeling that though Britain might eventually be victorious, a great deal of her strength would be sapped. The burden of war debts and rebuilding the country would be enormous. Her predominant position when she had stood alone in the early years of the war had changed and she had slipped to the position of the junior member of the 'Big Three'. There was already cries for independence from a number of countries of the Empire.

Ted grew melancholy as he came to the realisation that he was witnessing one of those major historical events: a shift in world power. A hundred and fifty years of Pax Britannica was waning and increasingly being taken over by the country he had left just two hours ago.

He decided these thoughts were driving him into a state of depression and that he had better counteract them. Wasn't it a fact that no Nazis were goose-stepping down Whitehall or occupying the castle in his hometown of Alnwick? Then with a shrug he quickly drove all pessimism from his thoughts with one reassuring solution, 'Let's get back and make sure we win this bloody war!'

Three and a half hours after leaving Windsor, they pulled into Union Station, Toronto. Sundays in Toronto were quiet, lonely and boring. One could hear one's own footsteps on the concrete sidewalk echoing between the blocks of buildings. All pubs and centres of entertainment were closed. To George and Ted, the city seemed even less inviting as their taxi sped them toward their digs. It was midnight, the streets were empty and dimly lit. Oh! what a contrast to the American city they'd left barely four hours ago.

The brightest spot in Toronto for the pair presented itself when they entered the brightly lit dining room of the digs. Voices and laughter filled the room as Chick, in an elegantly decorated dressing gown and looking like a Hollywood film director, was seated at the head of the table relating a story to seven or eight female lodgers attired in their nightdresses. With a quick spontaneous 'Hi!' from the girls and Chick, the newly-arrived pair's presence was acknowledged and the assembled group quickly returned to the matter at hand.

Ted would normally have felt snubbed, but he was very tired and glad not to have to answer any questions about their trip. So he and George headed straight for their room and bed.

Chapter 16

The Sweeper

Next morning the trio were informed that there had been a change in plans and they would not be joining the *Aries*. Instead they would commission HMS *Clinton* when she was ready at a later date. And so the artificers spent the working day going over every nook and cranny of their newly-assigned sweeper. Ted found that some shipyard workers had located one leg of the tripod mast in the wrong position, for the leg prevented the door to the captain's lobby from opening fully. No formal complaint was necessary for once Ted had donned his foreman's role at 4 p.m., he made sure his gang rectified the problem.

Toward the end of the first week after Ted's and George's return from the States, the General Manager of the yard asked Ted over to his office. Besides the General Manager, there were three other employees present. Ted recognised them as the night, morning and daytime superintendents. The General Manager welcomed everybody and immediately advised them about the reason for the meeting. He explained that the powers-that-be wanted a higher level of production especially from the daytime shift and suggested that the night and daytime superintendents combine their work forces, asking Ted if he would take over the night superintendent's job.

Of course Ted would. It meant a higher salary and the prestige of holding the top night job. The General Manager then told Ted that the previous night super would stay with him for the rest of the week to teach Ted 'the ropes'.

The speed of delivery of the minesweepers to the Royal Navy increased and Ted found that the greater part of his shift was devoted to making sure that all the required equipment, fuel, water, stores, instrumentation and food was aboard each ship as its trial date approached.

Just previous to trials of his own vessel, the *Clinton* was towed to dry dock. Actually it was two wooden floating docks joined end to end. The timbers were so old that pumps worked night and day to enable the docks to remain afloat.

The area was named Cherry Street. This was a misnomer if ever there was one, thought Ted, for not only was the stench from a nearby glue factory unbearable, but the taste it left in one's mouth was even worse. Added to this, the ferocity and numbers of the fly population might well have challenged the Egyptian plague. Ted made sure he spent as little time at Cherry Street as possible.

One of his last official jobs as shipyard officer was to prepare his own ship, HMS *Clinton*, for trials. On the night before he decided to put George in charge of fuelling the ship. During the early part of the evening Ted boarded the *Clinton* with the express purpose of instructing George on the correct procedure for fuelling ships so that she would remain on an even keel and trimmed correctly. Late that night, however, as he looked from his office window, Ted could tell that that pig-headed George was ignoring his instructions. The ship was heeling well to port. An hour later it was on an even keel, just after midnight the ship was heeling to starboard. And so the vessel's attitude oscillated all night. Ted thought, 'To hell with it,' as long as the vessel was fully fuelled and sitting square in the water when his shift finished. Fortunately he was able to report to his relief that the *Clinton* was in fact fully-fuelled and ready to go.

Using his official shipyard car Ted picked up George at the gangway of the *Clinton* and drove to the digs to get in a few hours sleep before they donned their uniforms and took up their official jobs as observers during the ship's trials. The ship was still under the control of the builders and so the trials were conducted by shipyard personnel.

Shortly after 9 a.m. the last line was hauled in. The sweeper slowly backed away from the dockside wall, turned and made her way across

Toronto harbour, then through the inner harbour and out into the waters of Lake Ontario. Some time was spent in testing the capabilities of outside machinery like the anchor windlass and the steering gear.

George was already involved in a confrontation with the operators of the forward boiler room as Ted stepped down amongst them. He had complained that the operators were causing the boiler to make black smoke, then went on to raise hell about the position of the fan control handwheel, saying that one shouldn't have to stand on a box to reach it. The three shipyard operators were not going to take any of his interference and let George know that they were in charge and he better get lost.

Ted took George to one side and advised him that they were there just as observers and if he noticed anything wrong, he should make a note of it and hand over his notes to the Engineer Officer at the end of the trials. The officer would then discuss the defects and any other problems with the shipyard management.

Ted then joined Chick down in the engine room where the engines were slowly being brought up to power. Chick requested the test personnel to let him look at the indicator diagrams taken from each of the three cylinders on both engines. He and Ted took the diagrams with them out onto the upper deck where they sat down and studied them.

Chick scanned the diagrams from the port engine and was satisfied that the engine appeared to be performing normally. However, Ted exclaimed, 'There's something very wrong with the high pressure cylinder of the starboard engine!' He pointed out to Chick that very little power was being developed in the high pressure cylinder and that the intermediate and low pressure cylinders were developing more power than was normal for the amount of the steam being admitted to the engine. Chick agreed with Ted's findings on returning the diagrams to the shipyard's personnel. The yard was obviously aware of the problem for the top man was already on the bridge and was advising him of the problem and saying that there was no point carrying on with the trials.

It was time for Ted to head for his shipyard office and off with his uniform when the sweeper pulled alongside the dock. Already there were written messages on his desk about the problem with *Clinton*'s starboard engine and about other defects. He dispatched a gang down to the ship with instructions to remove the combined high and intermediate valve cover and valves. At midnight Ted received a telephone call from the foreman on the ship, saying he thought he'd located the problem.

Ted headed down to the ship and engine room. Peering down into the valve chest, the foreman directed the beam of his flashlight onto an area halfway down. There was a rough ragged hole about four inches in diameter through the wall. It was a blowhole in the cast iron casting, obviously the result of poor casting procedure during manufacture. The hole would explain why steam was completely bypassing the high-pressure cylinder.

Owing to the location of the hole, it was a tricky operation to bore out the rough hole and to fit a well-fitting steam-tight plug. The procedure was time consuming and three days passed before the *Clinton* successfully completed her full power trials.

It was August and *Clinton*'s full crew were starting to assemble. Chick and Ted realised that they didn't have many more shopping days left before the ship sailed. So they spent any off-time they had wandering up and down the aisles of Eaton's department stores. Chick was more worldly-wise in the area of cosmetics, perfumes, lingerie and women's apparel than Ted, so Chick did all the advising.

And so Ted laid in a stock of Helena Rubenstein's 'Heavenly Scent', Eau de Cologne, nylon stockings, silk and satin underwear, the latest lightweight shoes, lipsticks of every colour, a manicure set, and a set of brushes and combs. Then they went to the food department and gathered up stocks of canned soups, tomato, orange, apple and cranberry juice, and canned apricots, pears and peaches.

Chapter 17

Bye, Bye, Toronto

The *Clinton* was commissioned at the end of August; Chick, Ted, and George had vacated their digs and taken up residence in the ERA's mess aboard their ship. They were joined by Buck Taylor, a Chief ERA, newly out from England; the Engineer Officer was a regular Royal Navy Warrant Engineer from the same artificer apprenticeship trained background as Ted. The Chief ERA's duties were that of the Senior Engineer.

The ERAs' mess was allotted one stoker who as a messman acted in the same capacity as a steward and kept the mess clean. Each ERA had a locker into which he placed his suit-case and all his worldly goods, including all the gifts and food that Chick and Ted had bought with the money from their non-Navy jobs.

Apart from Chick's gifts, Ted would, by chance, notice the stacks of Canadian paper money piled up on one of the shelves of Chick's locker; that singing job ashore must really have paid off!

With no minesweeping winch as yet installed, the vacant space made an ideal location on the minesweeping deck for shooting the official commissioning photograph as all ninety-three of the crew including six officers were caught in various poses and with different facial expressions.

Beside the Warrant Engineer the only other professional sailor among the officers was the Captain. Previously an officer in the Merchant Service he was now a Lieutenant-Commander RNR (Royal Navy Reserve). He also wore the DSC ribbon. The First Lieutenant, a Lieutenant RNVR

(Royal Navy Volunteer Reserve) was a tall well-built Canadian. There was also another Lieutenant RNVR, together with two Sub-Lieutenants RNVR.

A great deal of time was devoted to provisioning ship, and especially making sure that every space available was packed with those items of food unavailable in the United Kingdom.

The whole shipyard turned out to see the sweeper pull in her last line, her last connection with Toronto. She gave a prolonged blast on her sirens, the folks ashore cheered, waved, and clapped, and a band struck up with 'O! Canada', and 'God save the King'. Folks ashore were still waving as the *Clinton* passed out of the inner harbour, sailed through the Eastern Channel and turned into the outer harbour. It was a beautiful morning. The lake was as calm as a mill-pond as the sweeper gradually increased speed. The swishing sound of the water as it ran along the side of the vessel was almost therapeutic.

The Great Lakes certainly came by their name honestly, for after twelve hours of sailing from Toronto the sweeper was still making good speed eastward on Lake Ontario.

Early next morning the ship moved from the Lake and entered the St Lawrence river. For about sixty miles she navigated her way through the thousand-island section of the river. Ted had never before witnessed such magnificent scenery. The brown waters of the lake had changed to the brilliant sky-blue of the river; beautiful deep green trees crowded each and every island and the shore line; bright red rocks lined the water's edge of the islands and the banks of the river. Most of the larger islands had summer cottages built on them with a path running from them down to a landing stage at the water's edge to which leisure craft were moored. In the grounds of most cottages was erected a flag-staff from which the Canadian red ensign or the United States stars and stripes flew according to which side of the international boundary the island lay. Motor boats constantly sped back and forth amongst the islands. A blue haze with a distinct cooking smell drifted across the river from most of the inhabited islands; it was the Labour Day week-end and the Canadians and Americans were enjoying their traditional barbecue.

Ted dwelt on the irony of the scene, of a ship bristling with guns heading for war through the traditionally peacetime atmosphere of this beautiful river.

Chapter 18

'Shooting' the Rapids

Leaving the islands astern the vessel nosed its way towards a walled-in channel; as Chick and Ted watched from the port side of the minesweeping deck they noticed how the fast-moving current was causing the water to pile up against the buttress of the concrete wall. The ship started to pick up speed as it was pulled into the channel by the current. To the artificers it seemed that the vessel was getting out of control.

The constant clang of the engine-room telegraph made Chick race to assist George at the controls. Ted dashed aft to the steering-gear flat to ensure the steering-engine was working properly.

The power of the water moving down the channel was so overwhelming that even with the rudder hard over to port or starboard, and with one engine going full ahead and the other full astern, the rapidly moving water still dictated in which direction the vessel was going. Orders on the engine telegraph from full ahead to full astern became so rapid, that is, in a matter of seconds, that the normal procedure of shutting-off steam to the engine before putting the reverse engine in the ahead or astern mode was abandoned. In other words, with one movement of the reversing engine lever the engine would go from full ahead, would stop instantaneously and, with a bang, would immediately accelerate up to full speed in the opposite direction. To the artificers this treatment of the engines was almost criminal, and more like sabotage.

The vessel zig-zagged its way down the channel for over two miles until, to the relief of all, she was finally dumped into a calm bay at the end of the channel.

The experience had shaken the confidence of the artificers in their engines and their ship. Would she respond in the future to the propellers thrust ahead or astern?

It took some time before the surprise of the past experience wore off. The ship was now acting like a lady as she and the river seemed to respect each other.

However it was too early to be complacent; the *Clinton* suddenly gave a lunge forward, then started bumping and rolling violently from side to side. The engine telegraphs started going frantic again; this time all the artificers hit the engine-room plates including the Chief. Chick took the controls of the starboard engine, whilst Ted took control of the port engine. The Chief and George kept the boiler-rooms aware of demands for steam. As the ship bounced, wallowed, slid, rocked and rolled, Ted imagined he was on a roller-coaster ride.

The punishment the engines were taking was worse than before and the Chief was becoming concerned about how much more of this punishment they could take without a major breakdown.

After three-quarters of an hour, the vessel suddenly rose up violently, spun round, and then bumped which sent the engine-room staff flying forward. The telegraph rang down 'Stop', then 'Finished with Engines'; silence followed.

Chick and Ted went on deck. The sweeper lay up at the bows and the branches of trees were hanging over and shading her fo'c'sle. HMS *Clinton* had just 'shot' the rapids, and was now at rest in the whirlpool at the foot of the rapids. The artificers couldn't believe their eyes; a 1250 ton displacement vessel, 225 feet long and with a draught of almost eleven feet, 'shooting' a rapid?

Their disbelief soon turned to frustration when the Chief appeared with the news that the condenser was leaking. That meant that the cooling water from the river was leaking through the packing seals of the condenser tubes and into the ship's distilled feed water system, causing contamination.

It was a big repair job. The artificers worked throughout the night, hoisting the condenser's large end doors off, then testing and sealing the leaks. The damage had been caused by the overheating of the condenser, owing to the cooling pump losing suction having become blocked by sand during the 'shoot'.

Next morning the sweeper extracted her bows from the trees, after a prolonged full astern on both engines. It was a beautiful day and the vessel made good progress. Late in the afternoon, the artificer on watch felt a repeat of the ship's movements that had foregone the previous day's plunge into the rapids. It was in fact a repeat of yesterday's roller-coaster ride. The entire ERAs' mess took up their positions again in the engine-room, as the punishment was once again administered.

The day ended the same way: the bows of the sweeper dug into the shore-line of a whirlpool and the condenser leaking again. And so for two nights running the artificers went without sleep as they plugged the leaking condenser.

In a fit of anger nurtured by lack of sleep, Ted exclaimed, 'Whose side is this bloody Captain on, or is he in such a rush for more medals?'

The condenser once again repaired, the sweeper continued its journey to the sea. Another day passed and the vessel was making its way along a canal. Again Chick and Ted were on the minesweeping deck taking in the sights. They heard one ring on the engine-room telegraph but there was nothing unusual about that. After a minute or so, however, they were alarmed at the speed the vessel was proceeding down the narrow canal, such that a huge bow wave was being created and crashing against the canal side, sending a high wave of water ashore and causing people to run for higher terrain.

Ted and Chick flew down to the engine-room. George was on watch. 'What's up?' he yelled. Ted and Chick pushed by him, looked at the revolution indicator and, grabbing the throttle controls, reduced the speed of the engine to the 60 revolutions per minute as indicated.

George was furious, 'Who the hell do you think you two are? Wait till the Chief hears about this.'

Cautiously Chick placed his arm round George's shoulder and explained that he was supposed to be doing 60 revolutions per minute not 120. After calming down, George admitted he thought half-speed on the telegraph meant 120; Chick then explained that whenever half-speed was ordered, you followed whatever figure was shown on the revolution indicator.

Returning to the upper deck, Chick and Ted were suddenly alerted by two extremely loud blasts; turning towards the source, they saw the bow of a large laker in ballast towering fifty to sixty feet above the water, approaching them from around a bend in the canal. The sweeper slowed down to a crawl and moved to one side, almost scraping the wall of the canal as she did so. The vessels passed each other with barely inches to spare.

The pair tried to contemplate what might have happened if they hadn't throttled back the engine's speed.

Chapter 19

To Salt Water and the Sea

The sweeper moved from the fresh water of Lake St Louis, and was dropped 46 feet through two locks into the sea-water portion of the river at Montreal. She tied up against the wall of an open basin adjacent to a busy thoroughfare.

Montreal was a much more lively and bustling city than Toronto, and the crew could hardly wait to get ashore. At 1 p.m. the first crowd of libertymen raced down the gangway, and quickly disappeared into the bars, shops, and movie houses; some even did some sight-seeing from Mount Royal.

The scene was much different some ten hours later. There was the occasional straggler zig-zagging to find the first rung of the gangway, then a gang of four or five each supporting each other, caps pushed way back on their heads and singing, 'Fuck 'em all, the long and the short and the tall!' and so on. Arriving at the gangway they would indulge in theatricals. 'After you Charles,' said one, waving his hand towards the gangway and bowing; 'Oh no, Percival, after you; age before beauty!' would say the other; then one imitating a woman's voice and walk would push them all aside saying, 'Out the way, you silly twerps, don't you know your manners, it's ladies first!'; and so it went on until the duty PO yelled out, 'Jones, Martin, Clark, Wilson, Hall; get aboard!'

Two or three reported back aboard with black eyes and dried blood on their faces. Then a police van arrived. Two French-Canadian policemen alighted from the front and opened the back-doors of the van. Four bedraggled stokers fell out and were escorted by the police to the gangway who then turned the stokers over to the duty PO's custody.

Several libertymen did not return to the ship that night; instead the Captain had to go up to police headquarters next morning and bail them out. It is true that a number of *Clinton*'s crew were not angels, but a lot of French-Canadians nurtured a deep hatred towards the British, and especially the English, probably dating back to the defeat of the French at Quebec in 1759. Most of the sweeper's sailors were ignorant of this deep-seated hatred held by the French-Canadians and so it was that the slightest provocation, especially within the atmosphere of a bar, would set off a confrontation between the sailors and the local people. Unfortunately all the police were French-Canadians and they turned out to be more fanatical than the man in the street. Without listening to any explanation, they automatically went after the British sailors with their clubs and night-sticks.

After two days the sweeper slid out of Montreal and made for the sea. Half a day's sailing brought the *Clinton*'s port side under the shadow of the Heights of Abraham.

Looking up the steep, rocky Heights before him, Ted's mind was cast back to his early childhood in Greenwich, when his mother would take him for a walk up to the observatory and they would pass the statue of General Wolfe looking out and across the Thames below. His childish mind thought that the man looked too small and thin for a real General and in particular he remembered the General's long, thin, sharp-pointed nose. Still observing the heights Ted thought maybe it was an advantage to be small and thin in order to climb that rugged terrain. He even broke out into a sweat when he imagined dragging his two hundred pounds up to old Abraham's farm on top.

The old city of Quebec looked magnificent as the vessel passed into the ever-widening reaches of the river. A few hours later the river became so wide it was impossible to see the banks; in fact it looked and felt more like the open sea. Occasionally whales would rise to the surface, send up a spout of air and water and disappear beneath the waves again.

One of the seamen was complaining of severe pains in his stomach and after a time the Captain and First Lieutenant diagnosed that he was suffering from appendicitis and would have to be put ashore for treatment.

They hailed a large fishing boat, but couldn't get the skipper to understand. Eventually the First Lieutenant, in his best Canadian French, got the message through, and so the sailor was given a bumpy transfer.

A day after leaving Quebec city and heading into the Gulf of St Lawrence, the weather started to deteriorate. Thick black clouds loomed up on the horizon as the sweeper plunged her bows into heavy head-on seas.

Chapter 20

Engine Trouble

Some of the bearings of the starboard engine started to heat up. The artificer of the watch had a stoker constantly ensuring that the troublesome bearings had their oil-boxes filled at all times. More of the main bearings and eccentric straps started to build up heat. Four hours after the onset of the trouble, the various artificers of the watch became concerned about the amount of lubricating oil that was being used. The Chief ERA, after consultation with the Engineer Officer, issued orders that the use of lubricating oil was to be restricted and that cold fresh water was to be played on to the offending components. The cold water, though not the ideal lubricant, kept the bearings cool, but more and more quantities of fresh water were required to keep the temperatures down. The weather grew worse and the safety of the vessel demanded she continue to steam into the oncoming seas. The vessel could only produce so much fresh and distilled water, so the Chief ERA had the Chief Stoker shut off fresh water for the crew's requirements, and rationed each man to one bucketful a day.

Eventually concern grew that the boilers might go short of distilled water. The artificers fell back to the last resort and allowed salt water to be played on to the starboard engine's bearings. Salt water is the worst thing to come in contact with highly polished mild steel surfaces. Corrosion starts and heat causes crystals of highly abrasive salts to form.

Rounding the Gaspé peninsula the situation with the starboard engine was becoming critical. The soft solder-like white metal, which formed the surface on which the mild-steel crankshaft journals ran, started to melt and slither down the side of the bearing housings. There it re-solidified and hung like thin leaves of silver. The eccentric sheaves and straps which actuated the valve gear had their bottom halves surrounded by sheet-metal pans into which salt-water was now being poured. The rotating sheaves and straps caused the yellow scum-like mixture of salt-water and lubricating oil to splash and this slimy concoction was flung over the engines, the engine-room plates and the operators. With the white metal leaving the bearings the clearances were increasing and gradually a mechanical 'knock' developed in the starboard engine. The knock grew heavier and louder with every revolution.

As the *Clinton* moved further out into the Atlantic, Ted feared that every U-boat within a fifty mile radius would hear the sweeper's approach. The engines were now protesting the terrible punishment they had been subjected to during the 'rapids shooting' episode.

Ted lay in his hammock immediately on the other side of the engine-room's after bulkhead listening to the torture the starboard engine was going through at every revolution. What would happen when all the white metal had melted and steel started to run on steel? How long could this go on for without a major breakdown?

Each day seemed like weeks, but eventually the old girl headed south-west along the coast of Nova Scotia and crept into the naval dockyard at Halifax.

Ted almost felt a joint pang of relief with the starboard engine as the telegraph rang down, 'Finished with Engine'. If 'shooting' the rapids was supposed to save time, it didn't work out that way as far as the 'Old Lady' was concerned; it took weeks to rectify the damage to the starboard engine. Every connecting and eccentric rod was removed, along with every bearing, eccentric sheave and every other component attached to the starboard engine's crankshaft. The after-most journal of the crankshaft was found to be running one eighth of an inch out of truth, and had to be re-machined in place and reduced in diameter.

Chapter 21

Repairs in Halifax

During the spell in the dockyard, the Canadian Navy sent some of their young stokers and ERAs under training aboard *Clinton* to carry out some maintenance jobs. Ted got himself into some hot water with a Canadian Lieutenant-Commander for playing up hell about the amount of damage the Canadian stokers were inflicting on *Clinton*'s machinery. One case Ted cited was connected with finding the valve gear of two feed pumps bent and the pumps inoperable; the other involved the poor and unprofessional way the Canadian ERAs had re-packed various steam valves. The Canadian officer tore into Ted with, 'How do you expect my boys to learn?'

Ted retorted with, 'Let them learn elsewhere, preferably on your own ships.'

'What's your name?' barked the officer, 'You'll be hearing more about this!' he threatened, as he tore up the engine-room ladder. Ted didn't hear any more, and neither did any more Canadian Navy personnel venture aboard.

Occasionally Ted and Chick spent the evening at the Chief and POs' club; at other times Ted would accompany Chick to the Silver Slipper dance-hall, known to sailors as the 'Galvanized Boot'. There Chick would thrill all and sundry with his magnificent rendition of all the popular songs.

The shipboard living quarters of the three tiffies and the Chief ERA was an enclosed space ten by ten feet with a standing height of eight feet.

84

In comparison the Engineer Officer's cabin also occupied a space of ten by ten feet, and the officer's wardroom was twenty-three by fifteen feet, including the pantry. Besides being occupied by the Chief, three ERAs and a messman, the space was also taken up by a table, the Chief's easy chair, two seats, lockers, a bread locker, a long stool, a hammock bin for five hammocks, six lockers, a hat cupboard, a refrigerator, and a manhole coaming which stuck up eight inches above the deck, and over which everybody tripped at least a dozen times a day.

Most nights four hammocks were slung. Space was such that all hammocks touched each other, with the outboard hammock also touching the ship's side whilst the inboard hammock touched the bulkhead and was violently banged into each time the mess door was opened. In rough weather the impact of the outboard hammock against the ship's side was relayed through to all the other hammocks in sequence until the inboard one banged against the bulkhead, and then the whole sequence was reversed. Sleep was disturbed every time a tiffy climbed out of his hammock to go on watch and a few minutes later the disturbance recommenced as the off-coming watch-keeper climbed into his sack.

Mornings were a time when nerves became frayed. With eyes half closed, yawning occupants would swing or fall out of their hammocks to allow the messman to prepare breakfast. As they lashed their hammocks, the lashing would whip one of the others across the head or face, then they would push by each other to dump the hammock into its bin. Some would open their locker doors to get out their shaving and washing materials and in doing so bang somebody in the face or on the head with the door.

The Chief was a very religious man and he could usually calm down the temper tantrums; members of the mess respected him but were a little uncomfortable with his presence at times. They found it restraining and unnatural when they sometimes wanted to give vent to a gutful of blasting.

Each evening the Chief would get down on his knees in the mess, place his elbows on the bench seat, rest his face in his hands and pray in silence, while the remaining occupants would carry on with whatever they were doing or talking about.

85

While in Halifax, Buck (the Chief) went for long walks across the rugged heather moors north of the city. The landscape resembled parts of Scotland; perhaps that's why the province was named Nova Scotia.

It was well into autumn and there was a chill in the air and frost on the ground; Buck returned to the mess with a red glow on his face. Invariably he would raise his head and, sniffing the air, remark, 'This place has a bedroom smell!' as he moved over to the port-hole and threw the port wide open.

Shortly after the *Clinton* was commissioned the crew had the choice of opting for standard victualling or canteen messing. Canteen messing meant that the crew members of each mess were allotted the victualling allowance in money, and to it they could if they wanted add some of their own money to buy additional food from the canteen or ashore. The tiffies' mess decided to go for canteen messing, and elected Ted to be the caterer. Ted then asked if they wanted to eat well and if so would they be prepared to pay for the luxury; they agreed.

And so Ted made out the menu for each day and bought the necessary extras from the canteen and ashore. He then instructed the mess-man what the daily meals would be, and the mess-man would prepare the food on the mess table, mixing flour, water, and shortening to form the pie crust for shepherd's pie or steak and kidney pie. After preparing the food, the mess-man would then take it up to the galley to be cooked.

For a long time Ted had felt uneasy about having a certain messman prepare the food. Though he didn't pay much attention to rumours that circulated from the stoker's mess, he'd witnessed for himself while ashore that the messman seemed to latch on to homosexuals; so maybe the stokers knew better than Ted, when he heard the messman referred to as an arse-bandit by them.

This particular morning Ted made up his mind to relieve his anxiety as he watched the messman rolling, flattening, and pounding the dough with his hands and fists; and finally witnessing dough packed under his finger-nails.

Ted met up with the Chief Stoker on the minesweeping deck and made the excuse that he thought the messman was not the type to be a servant to a bunch of tiffies, and that the man was probably more fitted to be what he was supposed to be, a stoker. The Chief Stoker took it well, and said, 'Leave it to me!' Ted had an idea the Chief Stoker guessed the real reason.

That afternoon a little rubber-faced stoker came up to Ted saying, 'Chief! the Chief Stoker told me to report to you. I'm the new messman!' He was a cockney, he appeared to be void of all teeth, and his elastic-like lower lip turned up and almost touched his nose. The stokers had a befitting nick-name for him, Popeye, and so to the tiffies he became Popeye the messman.

A messman was probably the last job Popeye should have been recommended for; however he fell over himself in willingness to oblige. As the ERA's messman he was allowed, like the tiffies, to take his daily tot of rum neat. The rum ration was swilled down just before the mid-day meal; by meal-time Popeye was already swaying and tripping over things. One day he leaned over Ted's shoulder with a plate of pea soup into which he had his thumb immersed up to the last knuckle. Dumping the plate on to the table, he gave an intoxicated laugh and slavered all over Ted's neck. He continued his erratic path round the table dumping the various plates of food approximately in front of each intended recipient. After the mid-day meal ordeal, everybody moved out of the mess to give Popeye a chance to clear the table and clean up the mess.

Returning an hour later, however, Ted found the table and everything else in the same condition as when he had left. Popeye was lying on his back on the bench, snoring.

Ted decided he would hold Popeye's rum ration back until well into the afternoon when he had finished serving the mid-day meal and cleaned up the mess.

Breakfast the next morning provided another surprise. Ted was about to take a spoonful of sugar from the sugar-bowl, when he noticed that the bowl was full of water.

'Hi! Popeye,' shouted Ted. 'Where's the sugar?'

Looking into the bowl, Popeye exclaimed, 'Well, I'll be buggered, I put it into the fridge, and it melted!'

'What's it doing in the fridge, anyway?' questioned Ted.

'To keep it cool!' Popeye replied.

'Put it in the food cupboard in future!' retorted Ted.

Ted figured that the fridge had been turned off, and defrosting had caused water to form in the bowl and dissolve the sugar.

Popeye learnt slowly and gradually, and finally became an asset to the mess and to Ted the caterer. He actually became proud of his job, and thought it set him aside from the rest of the stokers. He particularly enjoyed the privilege and comfort of being able to get a full night's sleep every night, without having to go on watch; only 'Action Station' would spoil his routine.

George enjoyed his stay in Halifax. He fell in with a crowd of young Canadian Chiefs who enjoyed his company and so after a good night ashore he would stagger back aboard, slump into his hammock and sleep like a log until breakfast.

One night he must have imbibed too much or eaten some bad food. He had emptied the contents of his stomach through the open port of the mess but in the process his false teeth found their way to the bottom of the dock. Next morning Chick and Ted, who had spent the night at the Chief's club, found the diving-operations flag flying from the mast, and a diving boat moored adjacent to the port-hole of the mess. They couldn't believe their ears when a Canadian Chief Diver told them they were diving for George's teeth.

The dentures were eventually found. Ted tried to calculate how many sets of new false teeth could have been bought for the expense involved in recovering this badly worn set.

George and Ted decided they'd like to grow beards. In the Navy one doesn't just go ahead and do this, one has to put in an official request to see the Captain and get permission. Then, one doesn't just request to grow a beard, no! One requests, 'Permission to cease shaving.' A few days later the pair stood before the Captain and the Engineer Officer.

Looking toward the Engineer Officer, the Captain asked, 'Do you think the beards will get caught up in the machinery?'

The Engineer, with a slight smirk on his face, answered, 'Oh, no, Sir!'

Writing something down in the log, the Captain stood up and exclaimed, 'Request granted.' The tiffies saluted, turned about, and marched off.

It was now early December, the Canadian winter had set in, snow was everywhere and icy winds swept across the dockyard. The *Clinton*'s repairs complete, she put out to sea for trials. Both engines and the rest of the machinery performed satisfactorily. She returned to the dockyard for the night, and next morning she left Halifax for the United Kingdom.

Chapter 22

Back to the War

The *Clinton* headed for St John's, Newfoundland. Heavy seas were running when she approached the entrance to the harbour. Rocks lined both sides of the inlet and a swift current was running across the opening. Increasing speed, the sweeper made for one side of the inlet, but half-way through she was being swept toward the opposite bank. However her momentum saved the vessel from being thrust upon the rocks and she passed harmlessly into the sheltered waters beyond. She tied up at a dock at the head of the harbour and the Chief Stoker with four others commenced fuelling.

Ted stepped ashore and climbed up the steep streets of St John's. Most of the houses and buildings were painted white and the strong smell of fish filled the air. He didn't linger too long for the *Clinton* was due to sail before the turn of the tide.

Within three hours the sweeper headed out of the harbour and into the North Atlantic. The weather became progressively worse and Popeye had to damp down the tablecloth to prevent the dinnerware from sliding onto the deck. The *Clinton* was searching for an eastbound convoy which she was supposed to meet up with and join. The search went on night and day for forty-eight hours without sign or sight of the ships. It was forbidden to break radio silence and so, after wasting many hours and tons of fuel, it was decided she'd have to make her own way across the treacherous Atlantic.

At approximately midnight, two days after giving up the search for

90

the convoy, Ted was asleep in his hammock when he was suddenly wakened by a loud gushing sound like high-pressure steam escaping. Then he felt the whole ship give a shudder. Collecting his life-belt he rushed up to the minesweeping deck, thinking that the gushing noise could have been a torpedo. He stood looking down at the relatively smooth water and the moonlight dancing on the rolling waves. He couldn't see any sign of a submarine. Should he jump or not, he thought, glancing at his miserable looking life-belt with its perished and cracked rubber tube and the attached red lamp the battery of which had been dead for ages. Then he thought of the cold, cold, water. Was this the end?

After a few moments he noted the vessel didn't seem to be sinking and nobody was calling 'Abandon Ship'. The ship just lay dead and silent, rolling lazily. What a target for a U-boat, thought Ted as he moved quickly towards the engine room hatchway. Peering down he could see men running in all directions.

Before climbing down into the engine room, Ted's attention was drawn to the sound of heavy boots on the steel deck. It was Donaldson, a three-badge stoker (three badges meant he had had fifteen years of undetected crime). He was the oldest member of the stokers' mess-deck and the lower deck lawyer to most of the juniors. He was also the Chief Stoker's right hand man. As he pushed past, Ted noticed he had a wheel spanner and a pair of leather gloves in his hands.

'Where yer going, Donaldson?' queried Ted.

'Up to the fo'c'sle', he replied.

'What for?' yelled Ted and Donaldson raced on.

'To drop the anchor!' came back the answer.

Ted took after him shouting, 'Stop!'

As Ted caught up with him he said, 'You silly bugger, the anchor will never reach the bottom; it's over a mile and a half deep here!'

Donaldson grinned a little sheepishly and said, 'Please don't tell the Chief Stoker!'

Ted promised and the stoker returned to his mess.

Climbing down into the engine room, his feet landed into water lying to a depth of six inches on the floor plates. George in the nude was standing in the bilges at the after end of the space up to his waist in water. Every now and again he would put his head under water for a few seconds and suddenly reappear with various bits of debris and oily sludge clinging to his beard.

After surveying the scene, Ted suddenly came to the conclusion of what had happened. Debris from the builders yard and from the recent repairs in Halifax had blocked the bilge pump's suction system and prevented the pumps from discharging sea-water from various cooling systems and other sources pouring into the bilges from being pumped overboard. The level of bilge-water had steadily increased until it reached the main engine crankshafts. The rotating cranks started throwing water all over the engine room. Chick who was on watch had become concerned that the main switchboard and the electric generator would be put out of action, so he decided to open the main injection valve. This is a large valve which allows the ship's main circulating pump to take a suction from the bilges. In opening the main injection valve, insufficient sea-water cooling was being fed to the condenser so that exhaust steam from the main engines could not be condensed and steam pressure built up on the condenser, producing a back-pressure the reaction of which stopped the engines. The build up of steam pressure in the condenser had caused the safety relief valve to open, causing the loud gushing sound Ted had heard.

Stokers at the forward end of the engine room were engaged in opening the covers to two suction boxes. In them they found pieces of welding rods, wood, rags, matchsticks and empty cigarette packets. After the suction box covers were replaced. Chick started the bilge pump and gradually the water level in the engine room started to fall. George continued reaching down into the murky bilge water and clearing the end of the bilge suction pipe. By this time the water was down to his thighs and matchsticks, together with dirty brown oily scum, were entangled in his pubic hairs. Eventually all suction piping ends and boxes had been cleared and the water level reduced so that the engines could be restarted.

Ted had learnt a lesson. He immediately got a new life-belt from the stores and forever after made sure he had a fully charged battery in his belt's red lamp.

It was comforting to return to a warm hammock and feel the throb of the engines once again. The North Atlantic in winter lived up to its reputation. Heavy seas and high winds dogged the little sweeper the entire voyage. Ted and George's beards were well-developed and densely matted. They didn't have the misfortune of catching them in the machinery but they did get them saturated with sugee whoogee (a mixture of lubricating oil and water) flung out from the rotating eccentric sheaves of the engines as they gingerly placed the palms of their hands on the connecting rod big ends to sense the temperature. It took them ages to scrub the slimy yellow goo out of their beards after coming off watch.

Because of the wasted time and bad weather the voyage was taking longer than planned and fuel, water and lubricating oil were all becoming low. Something had to be done if they were to reach port. It was decided to reduce speed drastically, and all water and lubricating oil was rationed.

The *Clinton* limped into Moville, Northern Ireland with barely enough fuel to cover the bottom of the fuel tanks. The fast-flowing water out of Lough Foyle was a deep yellowish brown. The fields were a deep lush green and the air was invigorating, so different from the harshness of the landscape of Halifax they'd left over fourteen days ago.

Chapter 23

Two for Leave

After two days, the sweeper moved up Lough Foyle and the river to tie up alongside a dock wall in Londonderry. The three tiffies enjoyed their run ashore in this Irish city. The nearest pub was a matter of fifty yards directly across from *Clinton*'s gangway. The three found the inhabitants had a great sense of humour and a very descriptive way of expressing themselves. The Guinness stout bottled in stone jars tasted much better than any other Guinness the three had tasted. Ted also found a vast difference between the temperament of these Irishmen and those he had encountered in Detroit.

It was rumoured that ten days leave was to be given to each watch. It did wonders for morale, especially as it was getting close to Christmas.

Ted immediately went ashore and into the Irish countryside on the lookout for something to grace the Christmas dinner. He came across a farm alive with beautiful white-feathered chickens. Approaching the farm house he knocked on the door. An old shrivelled-up woman appeared. He asked her if she had any chickens for sale. She waved him into the room. It was very dark inside and Ted tripped as he stepped down and onto an earthen floor. Two oil lamps were burning on the mantlepiece. The mantlepiece also provided a roosting place for four or five chickens. Having accustomed his eyes to the dark surroundings, Ted could see several more chickens feeding off the floor of the room. The woman invited Ted to have a cup of tea. The kettle was already boiling on the open fire. Ted had never tasted such strong tea.

'So you want some chickens, do ya?' whispered the woman.

Ted nodded.

'How many?' she asked.

'Two big ones will be enough!' exclaimed Ted. Then he went on to tell her he wanted to take them home for Christmas.

She pointed to two chickens. 'What about them?' she queried.

'They're fine!' said Ted. 'How much?' he asked.

She waved her hand.

'Oh no!' said Ted, 'I'm fully prepared to pay.'

She continued to wave her hand and shake her head. Grabbing both chickens by the legs she wandered into the outside yard amid a flurry of flying wings and protesting squawks. After twenty minutes she appeared with a large bag and handed it to Ted, saying, 'Here you are, Merry Christmas!' She still refused money.

'Do you smoke?' asked Ted.

She reached down by the side of her chair and held up a long stemmed pipe. 'What about cigarettes?' asked Ted.

'Now and again,' she replied.

Ted reached into the pocket of his uniform jacket and planted four packets of duty free Senior Service cigarettes in her lap.

She looked down at them and finally said, 'God bless yer, laddie!'

He returned to the ship and placed the chickens in the freezer.

Ted wondered how his wife would react to his beard and became anxious in case she took a dislike to it. He decided to get the Captain's permission to recommence shaving if his wife objected to the beard. Permission was granted.

In the meantime Chick was becoming concerned about having to pay customs duties on all the goods he was taking home. He overcame the problem by contacting all the stokers living in the London area. Each one would transport their duty free allowance of goods to London and hand the items back to Chick once they reached the Big City. The plan worked for some goods, but unfortunately for Chick some of his exotic perfumes and scents ended up pervading the smoke-filled public and saloon bars of the Elephant and Castle and various other pubs either side of the Thames.

As the train chugged its way from Londonderry to Larne, Ted started to admire the reflection of his copper toned beard in the carriage window. At Carlisle he said, 'Goodbye! Have a Merry Christmas!' to Chick and left the train. He crossed the platform and waited for a train to Newcastle-upon-Tyne. Changing trains again at Newcastle, he headed for his home town of Alnwick.

His home was about a mile from the station. With a large sack of presents, food and other assorted items slung over his shoulder and carrying a suitcase, he realised he must have looked like Santa Claus to the townsfolk as he strolled through the familiar streets and passed equally familiar faces.

His wife's face lit up on first seeing him, but seemed reluctant to plant a really loving kiss on his hairy thickly matted face. His aunt thought he looked handsome with the beard; probably because it hid the less desirable features of his face, thought Ted. The gifts and especially the variety of foods totally unobtainable in Britain were viewed in wonderment and delight. Every now and again however Ted would notice his wife giving his beard quizzical side glances and he sensed she had made a decision and that decision would become known at the appropriate time.

Then the sweet talk started, with such statements as 'You looked so much better before you had that horrible beard.' His worst fears were realised. He retired to the bathroom and with lots of shaving soap lather and a new razor cut swathes through the beautiful copper-tinted beard. Looking into the mirror he didn't care for the end result. The skin at the original location of the beard was lily white while the rest of the face was a deep tan. On top of that the lily white area was covered with small bumps which resembled the appearance of a plucked chicken.

His wife's face betrayed a feeling of mild shock when he emerged from the bathroom and she quickly tried to defend her decision in the matter by reassuring Ted that within a couple of days he'd be looking like his old self.

Like all leaves the time flew by so quickly and once more Ted was making that long dreaded walk back to the railway station. This time his only piece of luggage, his suitcase, was empty.

Chapter 24

Working Up

The sweeper left Londonderry and sailed for a short distance round the coast to Harland and Wolff's shipyard in Belfast. There she had her minesweeping winch installed. Leaving Belfast the sweeper headed for Tobermory on the Isle of Mull in the Inner Hebrides.

Heavy seas were running as the vessel made her way between the islands. The midday meal was being served and Chick was spooning up his pea soup when, at the same time as the vessel lurched, an object fell into his plate sending a spurt of soup all over him. Pushing the object to the side for closer inspection, he suddenly jumped up in disgust. It was a set of false teeth.

George, seated at the other side of the table, reached across and extracted the teeth from the soup, exclaiming, 'I've been looking all over for those!'

Chick wiped himself down with a cloth, handed the plate to Popeye and demanded a fresh plate of soup. He spent the rest of the meal giving George a look of disgust. Apparently George had the habit of getting into his hammock, removing his false teeth and placing them on the tray carrying electric cables attached to the deck head. Popeye and George thought the whole episode amusing and rocked with uproarious laughter the moment Chick left the mess.

At Tobermory the sweeper engaged in anti-submarine working-up exercises. A submarine would move out into the open sea and dive. The *Clinton* would then have to track the sub with its ASDIC (Anti-submarine detection gear). Once the sweeper's detection gear established she was directly above the sub, she would drop small explosive charges to indicate she had located the underwater vessel. On some occasions Ted would be on watch in the engine room during some of these exercises when the bridge would call down to bring the sub 'up'. This entailed Ted taking hold of a length of steel piping and pounding the end of the pipe on the bilges three times. The sub's commander would hear the bang and bring her up. At first Ted got carried away with this jungle telephone system and gave the bilges a real pounding. Then he suddenly remembered that less than one quarter of an inch separated him from the sea.

The part of the working up exercises that George and Ted most enjoyed was enacting a surprise attack on the submarine as she laid attached to a buoy at night. They and others of the crew would pick a dark night when little or no moonlight was present. They would then get quietly into the whaler and softly row way out from the sweeper and approach the side of the sub farthest away from their vessel. A few yards from the sub they would pull the oars on board and let the whaler slowly drift until it gently touched the sub's hull. One member with two bags of flour in his hand would quietly make his way up to the conning tower and dump the flour down into the control room. A loud cheer would then go up indicating the *Clinton* had captured the sub.

Actually, most times Ted's crowd didn't manage to bomb the sub with flour. The sub's crew waited right up to the last moment and just before the invaders set foot aboard their vessel, all hell would let loose. The searchlights blinded the attackers and the powerful jets of water from the fire-hydrants set them sprawling into the bottom of the whaler as they struggled to grab their oars and row away like demons possessed.

During the passage to Stornaway on the island of Lewis in the Outer Hebrides, the Engineer Officer called Ted to his cabin and asked if the artificer could design and make a suitable decorative canopy for the electric fire in the officer's wardroom. Ted submitted a design which took the form of a polished copper canopy which would be fixed above the electric elements of the fire and project outwards and slope downwards from the fire. On the sloping copper canopy would be the ship's crest made in sheet brass and below the crest would be the ship's motto fashioned in brass wire and soldered to the canopy. The officer liked it and agreed that Ted should carry on, make and install it. Ted spent a great deal of his off-watch hours putting the project together and finally installing it. All the officers stood back and admired the improvement the canopy made to the wardroom setting. The Captain also voiced his admiration for the professional-looking job.

At Stornaway, the *Clinton* became a member of a minesweeping flotilla and gained valuable minesweeping experience in and round those waters.

The occupants of Lewis Castle in Stornaway through some source or other got to know of Chick's presence on the *Clinton* and one Saturday night he was invited to entertain the local laird and his lady and other Scottish nobles in the area during a major dinner dance function. A number of *Clinton*'s officers were also invited. Chick's description of the night's activities sounded like something out of Hollywood.

Two nights later the Captain and officers of *Clinton* invited a number of Stornaway's dignitaries and some Wren officers for a party on board. Ted's masterpiece above the electric fire became the focus of attention for two of the ship's officers and a Wren officer sat between them. The Wren officer suddenly declared there must be something wrong with her eyes, swearing she saw one of the letters of the motto at the bottom of the ship's crest move. The ship's officers sneaked a quizzical look at each other. Had she had too many pink gins?

'Look!' she screamed, pointing at the copper canopy over the fire.

'By God you're right!' acknowledged one of the lieutenants.

All three then concentrated their gaze at the scene before them. Suddenly all letters of the motto did a little swivel and, leaving a silver trail behind, slowly accelerated down the slope of the canopy and onto the deck. The letters were quickly followed by the crest itself.

By this time the hosts and guests had assembled to witness the strange phenomenon. The happenings became the centre of conversation and an excuse for another round of drinks.

The explanation was quite simple. Ted had attached the motto and crest onto the copper background with soft solder. The heat of the electric fire had caused the solder to melt, causing the motifs to become detached. Next morning he rectified the problem by re-soldering everything and attaching a thick sheet of asbestos beneath the copper canopy as an insulation against the heat.

It was Sunday and the sweeper was scheduled to take part in minesweeping exercises next morning. However a fuel pump had broken down and needed a new shaft. Chick went ashore to the one and only machine shop in Stornaway to see if he could use their facilities to manufacture the shaft. The shop was closed. After making enquiries, he was given the address of the owner. The owner answered the door dressed in his Sunday-best suit. Chick requested that he be allowed the use of his lathe. The man raised his eyebrows and in a broad Highland accent, roared. 'D'yer not know it's the Sabbath, man?' Pausing, he continued, 'Naebody works on the Lord's day.'

Chick, realising he was fighting a losing battle against the heavenly hosts, tried another tactic. He told the man that he and his whole family were ardent followers of the Lord and he was the solo tenor in his church's choir, and that the man was right and his mother and father would never allow him to work on Sunday. He went on to say that unfortunately the top man in Germany was the devil's disciple and did his evil work every day including Sunday and surely the bible taught us that the work of the devil had to be fought wherever and whenever it occurred.

The man listened intently, nodded now and again, then, pondering for some time, said, 'Alreet!' closed the door behind him and said, 'Follow me!'

Unlocking the big corrugated doors of the machine shop, the owner rolled them wide open. The bright morning sun shone through the doorway on to the lathe. Setting the old shaft down at the far end of the lathe, Chick placed a length of two-inch mild-steel round stock in the jaws of the lathe chuck and started machining.

Just after midday, men, women and children started to drift into the workshop and surround the lathe. Eventually the whole congregation from the church just up the road was crowded round Chick's working area. They were conversing among themselves in Gaelic, and giving Chick a look of disgust. Finally a tall, heavy-set man dressed entirely in black and with a black wide-brimmed hat, obviously the spokesman, stepped forward and, in the brogue of the area, directed his question to Chick, 'Do you no ken this is the Sabbath?' The crowd joined in with an approving mumble and nodded their heads.

Chick thought, here we go again. Turning to the owner of the machine shop he said, 'Mr Garvey, would you mind explaining to them the story I related to you before?' The owner nodded and, stepping up beside Chick, started talking to the crowd in Gaelic.

The assembly listened intently, giving an occasional nod and a wag of their heads. The explanation seemed to go on for ages. Eventually there was silence. Then they all started to talk amongst themselves. After a time they slowly sauntered out two and three at a time.

Next morning the *Clinton*, with her fuel pump repaired, sailed. After completing minesweeping exercises, she joined two other sweepers of the same class and all three made their way through the North Minch, eastward round Cape Wrath and toward the Pentland Firth. The sweepers were in line-ahead formation as they headed into the Pentland Firth.

The Firth was living up to its reputation. High winds blew the spray from the white-capped waves in horizontal streaks. The vessels buried their whole fo'c'sle deck right back to the forward four-inch gun down into the head-on seas and then the whole forward end would lift clear of the water, right back to the bridge. Moments later it would crash back into the sea with one great splash, sending plumes of white water speeding up and outwards.

Standing well aft by the depth charge rails and hanging on to the side rail for dear life, Ted was intrigued by the whole scene unfolding before him. As he watched, the stern of the *Clinton* rose up so high he could see the whole length of the fo'c'sle deck stretched before him and the sweeper ahead riding the next wave was positioned such that her fo'c'sle was at its zenith whilst her stern was practically submerged. The relative poise of the vessels at that moment allowed Ted to look down into a foot or two of the funnel of the preceding sweeper. Ted wished he'd had a camera to record the amazing scene. He thought that some day he could capture it in a painting.

Whilst in a pensive mood, he recalled how he used to suffer a mild touch of sea-sickness every time the county class cruiser *London* put to sea and yet the *Clinton* could stand on her end and it didn't affect him one iota. That's not to say he wouldn't rather have smooth sailing. Bad weather on a little sweeper caused many discomforts. When Ted got down on watch, he found the violent pitching of the vessel was causing the engines to race as the propellers came out of the water.

Once passed Duncansby Head and heading south, the weather and seas moderated and the sweepers were able to remain in perfect line-ahead formation. Entering the Firth of Forth, they headed for the minesweeping base of Granton. It was from this base that the sweepers would head out to the mouth of the Firth just off the Bass Rock and hone up on their various types of minesweeping skills. For weeks they would leave Granton at the crack of dawn, work up all day and return at dusk. Sometimes they would anchor overnight in the Firth.

Chapter 25

One Tiffy Down

During this period, the *Clinton* contracted condenseritis. Salt water was leaking though defective tubes and tube-end seals into the distilled feed water system and she proceeded to Henry Robb's shipyard in Leith for repairs. Chick and Ted took advantage of this period and found hotel accommodation for their wives in nearby Edinburgh.

Each afternoon Ted would take his wife for a typical four o'clock English tea at the Brown Derby on Princes Street. His wife Senta was pregnant at the time and demanding exotic foods, some of which were totally unavailable in wartime Britain. However, Ted was able to track down a supply of peaches at two shillings and sixpence each. He was also able to get some canned fruit and vegetables from the ship.

All three tiffies spent their midday meal in a cosy pub directly across the road from the shipyard gates. George would also spend most of his evening there or in another pub called Matelot Meg's at the top of Leith Walk.

Ted crossed the road from the shipyard gates to the pub opposite. He looked down the road where red-brick warehouses lined either side and recollected the nights at the early part of the war when German bombers set all the warehouses alight. Sheets of flames used to shoot hundreds of feet into the air as millions of gallons of the finest Scotch whisky went up in flames. Many a local from Leith and Edinburgh would lie on his stomach lapping up the scotch as it flowed freely down the gutters and into the sewers.

The *Clinton*, fully seaworthy, left Leith and proceeded further up the Forth, beyond the Forth Bridge to the minesweeping base of Port Edgar. Here she provisioned and got ready for her real job, clearing enemy mines of every variety. Buck Taylor, the Chief ERA, was relieved by a much younger Chief by the name of George Barlow. Ted had known him when he had been a Petty Officer apprentice and two classes senior to Ted in the 'boys'.

Chick also received a draft chit. He was to report to the Royal Naval Barracks, Portsmouth, for an officer training course. Ted felt sorry to learn that Chick and he were about to finally part company.

That night they decided to have one last good run ashore up in Edinburgh. Chick was excited about his new appointment and told Ted he always imagined himself walking up and down Bond Street in one of those naval officers' great coats.

Next morning Ted helped him carry some of his gear to the naval van at the head of the pier. They shook hands and Chick shouted to Ted, 'Hi! you there. What about chopping me off one!' With that Ted gave him an exaggerated salute and Chick returned it with a leisurely two-finger boy scouts' salute. They both laughed and he was off.

Chapter 26

To Gib and the Med

Early in July 1944, *Clinton* made her way out into the North Sea and turned south. Ted recognised Holy Island, Bamburgh Castle and the lighthouse on Coquet Island as the vessel steamed along the coast of his native Northumberland.

Next morning the sweeper was nearing the Thames estuary and Ted was on deck. Every now and again he could hear a strange putt-putt sound similar to a single-cylinder motorbike engine. It seemed to be coming from some low clouds hanging just above the mast. Then he caught sight of a black object with short stubby wings and pipe-tail, heading directly westward. This followed the description of a flying-bomb, aka a V1, aka a doodle-bug, aka a buzz-bomb, he had heard about on the BBC news bulletin. It was obviously heading toward the London area.

As the *Clinton* steamed south across the Thames estuary, she had to change course several times because of the vast amount of sea traffic. She was among a huge variety of vessels involved in the Normandy invasion. As Ted viewed the mass of ships, he particularly eyed the large landing craft and wondered which one Chick might have been on. If he was on one he couldn't possibly miss seeing *Clinton*'s huge pennant number J286 painted on her sides. He kept looking until well past the Channel Islands, but to no avail.

In mid-July the *Clinton* arrived at Gibraltar and lay alongside the wall. At night Ted would lie in his hammock and look through the open port and see the lights of Algeciras, Spain across the bay. He wondered how many enemy agents equipped with powerful binoculars were eyeing the Rock at that moment. All night long motor-boats would drop explosive charges into the waters of the bay and inner harbour to ward off enemy frogmen from attempting to place limpet mines under or on the hulls of the Allied ships. Every now and again, Ted would wake up and imagine he saw the goggled face of a frogman peering through the porthole.

Sometimes it was almost impossible to get a full night's sleep in the ERAs' mess, especially in a harbour like Gibraltar, for apart from the explosive charges going off all night, the returning libertymen's boots would ring on the steel deck above and the noise became even worse as they came clanging down the steel ladder and on to the mess-deck. On top of that, returning shore-goers always unloaded most of their bodily intake into the WCs directly above the mess. The flushed solid and liquid material would then be sent gurgling and banging down pipes which ran across the deck-head, a matter of a foot or so above the face of the tiffy trying to sleep in his hammock.

One night, George and Ted went up to the Garrison Sergeants' Club. There Ted met one of his classmates who had arrived that day on a destroyer. In the course of relaying all the news from home, he suddenly mentioned that Chick Henderson (Sub-Lieutenant Rowntree) had been killed. Ted was shocked. 'How? When?' he asked in quick succession. Apparently Chick had been in his room at the Royal Pier Hotel, Southsea, on the night of 25 June, when an object flew through the window and struck him in the stomach. Some people said it was a piece of shrapnel from our own ack-ack guns. Others said it was a piece of material from a flying bomb. Ted asked if they took Chick home for burial.

'No!' said his friend, 'He's buried at Gosport behind the Haslar hospital in the naval cemetery.'

George didn't believe it when Ted told him about Chick. It was the only time Ted had seen tears in George's eyes. They walked back to the ship saying very few words. Ted wondered if Chick ever got to wear his officers' greatcoat whilst walking down Bond Street. Ted told Popeye about Chick's death as soon as he got on board and within a few minutes it was the topic of conversation throughout the *Clinton*.

It took Ted a long time eventually to fall asleep that night. Thoughts came and went, like, 'Chick never got to be the Engineer Officer of one of those landing ships,' and 'Chick was already dead when the *Clinton* passed the invasion fleet.' He also wondered how Pamela his wife and little daughter were taking things. Chick could probably be still lying in his hammock next to him if that stupid officers' course draft chit hadn't come through. And so it went on until his brain became tired and confused.

At the end of July the *Clinton* in company with two other sweepers of the 5th MSF (Minesweeping flotilla) arrived at the Italian naval base of La Maddalena, a small island lying between Corsica and Sardinia. A piece of paper on the ship's notice warned all libertymen that relationships ashore were very tense and any drunkenness might start a shooting affray. The notice went on to warn that venereal disease was very prevalent and if personnel could not abstain they should use the licensed brothel. Allied and Co-belligerent officers were to be saluted at all times. Libertymen were further warned to protect themselves against malaria.

George and Ted stepped off the ship's gangway and walked up the dry, dirty and dusty road into the main part of town. The streets were crowded with hundreds of sailors. Ninety per cent of them were Italians and were the crews of the Italian Navy who had surrendered to the Allies. Ted and George became tired of saluting Italian officers; it was nothing to pass dozens upon dozens of senior officers within the length of one street and at least ten or eleven admirals. The senior officers would parade back and forth up the main street, three or four abreast, their arms intertwined and holding long cigarette-holders in their mouths. Some wore monocles and most had their uniform coats draped over their shoulders with the sleeves hanging loose by their sides, arm-less. To Ted they looked like a bunch of Hollywood actors taking part in an opera and awaiting their turn to go before the cameras. All the time the groups of Italian officers would stroll back and forward up the same street. They would be totally immersed in deeply intense and animated conversations.

It was on this island that Mussolini had been kept prisoner just before the Germans managed to engineer his escape.

Ted and George didn't particularly like the taste of the local wine although it was very potent. The thing that put them off were the glasses they drank from. Ted knew there was little or no fresh water on the island as he watched the tavern owner wash the glasses in a basin of murky-looking water and set before them a pair of glasses still thinly coated with a residue of red scum. Back aboard, the two tiffies took a shower to rid themselves of the brown sticky dust of the island.

The three sweepers were now joined by the senior officer of the 5th MSF in his sweeper, HMS *Larne*. For three days the flotilla swept the Bonifacio Straits between Corsica and Sardinia and managed to cut only two mines.

Early in August the *Clinton* and two other sweepers left Maddelena and arrived at Propriano, Corsica.

Chapter 27

Operation 'Dragoon'

All three vessels anchored in the middle of a huge bay. They lay there for two days. Ted wondered why they were idly swinging round the anchor in this deserted stretch of water. In the meantime George decided to go for a swim. He clambered up onto the wing of the bridge, jumped off and struck the water along the entire length of his stomach and chest with a terrific-sounding smack.

'My God!' thought Ted to himself, 'He's probably split his stomach wide open!'

He hadn't; for George suddenly surfaced and with his daredevil grin invited Ted to join him. More to answer the challenge than with the desire to swim, Ted jumped in. George swam for the shore. Ted followed. After a while Ted realised the shore must be over a mile away and he wasn't the strongest of swimmers. He looked back at the ship. It was even further away than the shore, so the shore it would have to be. He started to think about sharks. He was terrified of the monsters and put on a burst of speed, then realised he'd never last at that pace, so reverted to a steady stroke.

George reached the beautiful wide stretch of golden beach well before Ted. Eventually the straggler crawled ashore, exhausted, and lay for ages recuperating. He didn't have the nerve to look at the ship yet.

This was the birthplace of Napoleon. Ted wondered if the Emperor had ever played on this beach. This island was also the home of the Maquis (a secret force of French patriots). The name meant brushwood and Ted could see miles of it skirting the inner stretches of the beach.

Finally Ted took a look at the *Clinton*. She'd never looked so small to him. How the hell was he going to get back? No boat was going to fetch him so, walking as far as he could into the water, he started to swim and swim and swim. The sweeper didn't seem to get any nearer. If he didn't look at the ship and just concentrated on his swimming, it might help. It seemed like hours before he made a desperate grab for the bottom rung of the ship's ladder. Flinging himself on the mess-locker, he fell asleep.

On the second day the three sweepers were joined by two more of the 5th MSF, but the two newly-arrived sweepers were not what drew Ted's attention. The bay was filled with vessels of all descriptions: battleships, cruisers, destroyers and dan-layers. In the afternoon of the next day, the entire assembly of ships slowly sailed out of the bay. It was the beginning of the invasion of the South of France.

The *Clinton* moved slowly all day. Ted slept on the upper deck that night, waking periodically to listen to the slow throb of the engines and the slurp of the water against the sweeper's side as she moved slowly through the water.

At six o'clock in the morning all hell was let loose as the five sweepers doing a Russian sweep (rush in, rush out) cleared a path close to the Iles d'Hyères and towards the approaches to Toulon. This cleared area was to provide an operational area for the French cruiser *Lorraine* to use for bombardment. A German battery way up by Toulon started shelling the sweepers. They turned with sweeps still out and disappeared under cover of smoke laid by motor launches.

Heavy thunder clouds formed, heavy rain swept the area and the barrage balloons floating high above the landing craft started to be hit by lightning. They burst into flame and slowly collapsed and drifted down into the sea. Enemy aircraft managed to set some balloons on fire but the majority became victims of the lightning. The approaches to the beaches became laden with all sorts of floating debris. Ted noticed dozens and dozens of American 'K' rations drifting about.

The sweepers carried out another three runs westward past the Iles d'Hyères as far as the approaches to Toulon. Each time they came within

111

sight of the city, a particularly annoying German battery would open fire and each time the sweepers would turn away under a screen of their own smoke. The stoker POs in both boiler rooms, on receiving the order 'Make smoke' from the engine room, would open a valve which allowed cold fuel oil to be sprayed into the furnace. The inefficient combustion of the fuel would cause massive rolling clouds of thick black smoke to pour out and backward from the funnel. During one of these smoke-making operations, the fuel-oil had coated the inner lining of the *Clinton*'s funnel and caught fire. The flames licking aft from the top of the funnel engulfed the battle ensign which was flying on a gaff behind the funnel. Instantaneously the ensign was reduced to ashes. Donaldson, the three-badge stoker, now the proud owner of a beard and looking like a sailor on a packet of Capstan cigarettes, decided it was time to put out the funnel fire and so with the fire hose over his shoulder he moved toward the ladder leading up the funnel. Putting his foot on the bottom rung he had barely put his hand on another rung when he gave out an almighty scream. The red-hot steel rung had burnt his hand causing a sizeable blister. Poor Donaldson had been thwarted again.

During the last run by the sweepers up the approaches to Toulon, Ted saw tail-end Charlie (the last of the line of sweepers) move to starboard and lay a course toward the city and the German nuisance battery. The Captain of the tail-end Charlie was an Australian and he possessed a beautifully-shaped Alsatian dog. At this time the dog was standing erect like a mascot on the roof of the anti-submarine office in front of the bridge. The sweeper increased to full speed and suddenly the 4-inch gun started firing rapid rounds of shells. For the whole period the dog remained statue-like and looking in the direction of the firing. The German battery fell silent. The Australian skipper turned 180 degrees and headed back to his position in line with the flotilla. During all these sweeping operations, the big British, American and French cruisers were hurling tons of shells into Toulon and the coastal areas. The shells were passing directly over the masts of the sweepers. Ted hoped and prayed that the cruiser's gunnery officers knew their job. The shells sounded like an express-train passing overhead as they raced in toward their targets.

During the operation the sweepers had fired almost two hundred 4-inch shells. Unknown to Ted and most of the servicemen involved in the invasion of Southern France (called 'Operation Dragoon') the whole operation was being watched by Mr Winston Churchill in a destroyer.

Many years after the war and because of the success of MSF5 during 'Operation Dragoon', the French government awarded the Senior Officer, Commander Jenkins, the Croix de Guerre. Commander Jenkins always regarded the award as for the flotilla and not personal.

Chapter 28

Malta, Two Tiffies Down

The *Clinton*, together with the 5th minesweeping flotilla, arrived back at La Maddalena and continued sweeping the Bonifacio Straits for about a week, after which they sailed for Malta. During the passage to Malta, Ted, in his capacity as caterer of the mess, informed the members of the amount of money they owed to the canteen messing fund. It was generally a routine matter once a month; sometimes the members received a slight credit and sometimes they owed money. On this occasion George wanted to know why he owed money, so Ted showed him the catering book and tried to explain the expenditures. George would have none of the explanations and eventually accused Ted of stealing supplies, saying that he had seen him taking stuff ashore when he had his wife up in Edinburgh. Ted admitted that George was correct; however he always deposited the price of the goods into the canteen fund.

George remained stubborn about paying his debt and stated he wanted to see the Captain. Ted didn't particularly like the embarrassment of being dragged up in front of the Captain on this matter: however, it had to be. George made out his request to see the Captain and handed it to the Chief ERA. The Chief tried to persuade him about the foolishness of pursuing the matter, as did the Engineer Officer, but George was dogmatic.

Both tiffies came before the Captain next day. George repeated his story about Ted taking stuff ashore to his wife. In the end, the Captain said to Ted, 'Is this true?'

'Yes, Sir!' replied Ted.

'No matter if you paid for the goods, you are not allowed to take provisions ashore!' said the Captain.

The Captain then dismissed Ted. Ted didn't hear what went on between the Captain and George. However, when George returned to the mess, he reluctantly threw the money he owed the canteen fund onto the mess table in front of Ted without muttering a word.

Later on the Chief told Ted that George's shore leave had been stopped for ten days. Once again Ted wondered why George insisted on pursuing a path that, apart from embarrassing Ted, would have affected his future career. Thank God for a wise Captain, thought Ted.

The wharves, quays and creeks of the Grand Harbour of Malta were lined with hulks, some partially sunk, others with just the bridge and masts sticking above the water. Two or three large burnt-out and rusty tankers lay listing and tied up fore and aft to buoys. Ted took the motorboat up into the dockyard to get some evaporator coils repaired. Walking past the officers' gangway of one of the large cruisers, he saw a familiar figure stepping ashore. It was his old Divisional Officer from his boy apprentice days, now Commander (E) Philby, pukka as ever in his immaculately-tailored uniform and carrying his gold-knobbed walking cane. The two recalled old days and informed each other about this and that ex-apprentice being killed or lost on such and such a ship. In the end the Commander took his leave with, 'Well! I must be off,' and ended by saying to Ted, 'Why aren't you a Warrant yet?'

As Ted continued toward the coppersmith's shop, he thought to himself, 'I'll never be a Warrant if I get caught up in any more episodes like the latest one with George.'

After a day or so the *Clinton* moved out of the Grand Harbour and tied up fore and aft to the buoys in Sliema Creek. As Ted hailed a *dhaighsa* to row him ashore to Sliema Wharf, he caught sight of George sitting on a bollard on the upper deck. George had a mean look on his face and glared at Ted with a hateful stare in his eyes. He was taking his confinement badly.

Ted boarded the little green bus for Valetta. The heat was intense and though all the windows were wide open they made no difference to the discomfort. Every seat of the bus was occupied. The bus stopped and a young well-shod priest of about twenty-four years of age climbed aboard. The priest looked up and down the length of the bus, then an old wrinkle-faced fragile woman dressed completely in the traditional black attire and with a fully-laden basket on her lap struggled to her feet and stood to one side as the priest lowered himself gently into her vacated seat. The woman, barely able to stand, nodded and smiled at the priest as though it was a privilege to make the sacrifice. The scene made Ted feel sick.

Alighting from the bus, Ted made his way down the narrow streets of Kingsway, made narrower still by the massive white soft sandstone blocks and burnt-out bulks of timber lying everywhere amongst the rest of the rubble. There was scarcely a building left standing. On any length of wall left standing was painted the words, 'Bomb Roma'. St Paul's, the huge cathedral, was a gutted shell but Queen Victoria still occupied her perch, looking out with a defiant look on her face.

Families were living in shacks made of flattened large tin cans and from wooden boxes. The smell of burning kerosene or paraffin, the standard cooking fuel, was everywhere. There were no cats and very few other animals about. They'd all been eaten.

After partaking of two bottles of Cisk (the salty local beer) in a restaurant just behind Victoria's statue, Ted made his way to the ERAs' club in Floriana. Picking his way amongst the piles of jagged sandstone blocks and twisted and rusting iron railings, he saw the isolated building housing the club suddenly stand out in the sea of desolation.

It was a whole different world inside the club. The rooms were well-lit; there was a steady flow of conversation and laughter. Some of the tiffies were scribbling letters at the writing desks, others were reading, some were playing billiards, others were having a meal in the dining room and a goodly crowd stood and sat at the bar. Ted spent the first hour or so renewing acquaintance with many ex-boys from the *Caledonia*. He noticed a good number of them were wearing the BEM (British Empire Medal), some the DSM (Distinguished Service Medal) and some were wearing both, especially the submariners.

Somebody yelled, 'What yer going to have, Ted?'

'Let me see!' replied Ted.

'Have you ever tried the middle shelf?' someone cried.

'What the hell's that?' queried Ted.'

'Give the man a middle shelf!' someone cried.

'Cheers!' said Ted, lifting the glass to his lips.

The drink tasted good, but was strong. The drink was apparently a mixture taken from every bottle on the 'middle shelf'.

Eventually the ex-boys got round to asking have you seen so and so lately, and where is so and so now? At the end of the evening, Ted had figured that at least thirty out of his division of eighty had been killed or lost. There was a big toll of those who had volunteered for submarines. Ted knew the ones who would join submarines before they themselves would, for he used to watch the intent expression on their faces as an old submariner, Lieutenant (E) Joe Manley, used to while away half of the time allotted to a lecture on Marine Engineering on stories of his experiences on World War I submarines. The artificer apprentices used to lap up every word that fell from his lips.

Ted left the club and slowly picked his way through the ruins to the tip of Valetta and took a *dhaighsa* back to the *Clinton*. There was a full moon and the sound of the steady soft splash of the oars sent him to sleep before arriving at the ladder of the ship.

During this period the *Clinton* with the rest of the flotilla would carry out extensive minesweeping operations round the Maltese Islands. This was essential owing to the large quantity of mines laid by enemy aircraft.

The sailors' favourite name for Malta was 'bells and smells'. Apart from these and the heat, Ted enjoyed Malta and to some extent so did George, for though he wasn't allowed ashore for ten days, he was allowed to swim off the ship and spent many hours swimming round the ship while she was moored in Sliema Creek. Ted also took to swimming in the creek until he became aware of large ugly pieces of human waste floating around in large quantities and made the discovery that open sewers emptied into the waters. He never ventured into the creek again.

Ted found it entertaining occasionally to take a walk down Strada Stretta (meaning Straight Street of Steps), universally known to sailors

117

as 'The Gut'. Each side of the steep narrow street was a continuous row of bars, each separated from the next by a common wall. The majority of bars were named after one of His Majesty's ships. The bar Ted headed for was called the Lucky Strike. As far as he was concerned it had one entertainer who possessed a much greater talent than most of the other bars. His name was Bobby. He was a he but one would hardly know it from his attire. Some said he had been the organist at the big cinema in Tottenham Court Road. However it was his talent as a professional pianist that attracted Ted. The entertainer could switch from Beethoven's 'Moonlight Sonata' to 'As time goes by' at the call of a patron. Ted loved the way he played the 'Warsaw Concerto'. Most of the time Bobby dressed in a Carmen Miranda outfit.

Ted was sitting in the Lucky Strike one afternoon when Bobby swept in in a great flurry. Parading round Ted's table, he said, 'How d'you like my new shoes?' He was wearing a pair of women's shoes with heels at least three inches high and sparkling with multi-coloured stones. After some time Ted realised Bobby wasn't seeking Ted's approval so much as he was showing off in front of the bar-girls. There was a sort of professional jealousy between them.

Ted's wife, rather than laugh when he recounted the Bobby story, would give him a look of disgust and accuse him of being a latent homosexual, especially when Ted showed her the earrings Bobby had given him as a parting gift.

In mid-September 1944, Ted said goodbye to George for the last time. A draft chit had arrived for him and he left. The *Clinton* together with the rest of the flotilla also left Malta for Greece.

Chapter 29

Sweeping the Approaches to Piraeus

Two days afterwards, the flotilla started to sweep the Kithera Straits running between southern Greece and the island of Crete. A few old German mines were destroyed. The *Clinton* then landed a company of about ninety Royal Marine Commandos of the island of Kithera.

A day after Ted went ashore there, the Germans had already left and the Greek inhabitants had hanged their collaborating Mayor on a lamppost on the jetty. It was a hot afternoon and the sun blazed down. The village was situated on the side of a very steep hill with one main unpaved dusty street running through it. Little Greek and British flags hung from the windows of every house and donkeys with large wicker baskets on their sides passed up and down the street. The shrill chirping mating call of thousands of cicadas from the surrounding olive trees was deafening.

Perspiration was running freely from Ted's head and brow and ran into his eyes, blurring his vision as he reached the village square. He sat at a rough table under a tree. The owner of the taverna approached him holding a tray on which were three or four bottles and a glass; one bottle was water, of which Ted drank half a glass. From the other bottles he eventually settled on trying the light yellowish resin-like-smelling wine. It was the traditional Greek drink, retsina. Ted had no Greek money, so offered the Greek Maltese money. The man waved it to one side and re-topped Ted's glass.

During the next two weeks, the flotilla continued to sweep channels up the east coast of the Greek mainland and cleared the approaches to the island of Poros and the port of Piraeus. At the end of September each ship of the flotilla carried a company of Greek troops who were landed and took over the occupation of Poros.

The *Clinton* and the rest of the sweepers then set sail for Alexandria. 'Good oh!' thought Ted, 'A nice run ashore in Alexandria.'

Alexandria didn't appear to have suffered too much from the ravages of war, apart from the damage caused to a number of British warships by Italian frogmen. The streets were swarming with servicemen, pedlars and horse-drawn carriages. The air was filled with the pungent smell of gardenias.

Ted made his way to the Sergeants' and WOs' club. It was a palatial building; the Egyptian waiters were dressed in white smocks with red fezzes on their heads. The bar was stocked with every conceivable drink, the most popular at the time being any one of three named the Roosevelt, the Churchill or the Stalin.

Like all visitors to Alexandria, Ted was eventually persuaded by a very persistent pedlar to buy a camel-skin suitcase.

Unfortunately in less than forty-eight hours the flotilla was ordered to sail; they were part of the force known as 'the return to Athens' and named Operation 'Manna'.

Chapter 30

Operation Manna

In the early hours of Sunday 15 October, with a heavily overcast sky and occasional rainstorms, the *Clinton* and the rest of the 5th Minesweeping Flotilla led a vast variety of ships to the rendezvous outside Poros Bay. The ships included the British cruisers *Orion*, *Sirius*, *Aurora*, *Ajax* and the *Black Prince*, destroyers and landing craft, together with the old Greek battleship *Averoff* which during the voyage from Alexandria found it hard to exceed 8 knots, all the time sending up great thick black columns of smoke from her three funnels.

At about 7 a.m. the sweepers ran into a field of mines and during the next hour managed to cut twenty-five of them loose. In the meantime Ted saw three or four wooden motor launches blown sky high and come sprinkling down into the water like so many giant match-sticks.

Just before Ted went down into the engine room for his 8 a.m. to noon watch, he was watching a large tanker to starboard. As he watched there was a tremendous orange flash followed by an ear-splitting explosion, then silence. Where the tanker had been a second before there was nothing. Ted took up his position between the two engines. Within five minutes of being on watch he heard a crack like a revolver going off, followed by a tremendous explosion. The lights went out momentarily, various types of loose hardware like nuts and bolts rained down and his head struck an overhead hand-wheel. Positioning himself away from any overhead object, he spread out his arms and grabbed the stop-valve of both engines. The revolver-like crack and following explosion continued as mine after mine blew up. Mines were exploding at a rate of about one every five minutes. Any glass in the engine room was shattered by now. The whole experience was becoming so nerve-racking that Ted began to think, 'Let's get hit and get out of this crazy situation.'

The Engineer Officer then appeared in the engine room. He gave Ted a half-reassuring smile. Ted took him by the arm and said, 'I wouldn't stand there, sir, I just cracked my head on that valve.' The engineer nodded and moved to one side. At that moment there was the biggest explosion Ted had ever heard. The *Clinton* lifted and shuddered; all the lights went out. It was obvious that she had been hit.

The Engineer Officer told Ted to go forward and assess the damage. As he got to the main deck and started to walk forward, the sweeper took a sudden plunge and Ted found himself being accelerated into a trot in the forward direction. When he reached the cabin lobby all the lights were out and he was falling over rifles which had been dislodged from their racks. He found the water-tight hatches to the seamen's and the POs' lower messes distorted, allowing air to escape. He quickly got some stokers to cut up lengths of four by four wooden shores and jammed them between the hatch covers and the deck-head above.

Ted, realising that the forward bulkhead of the boiler was now exposed to the forces of the sea, set about reinforcing it. Hastily recalling the lessons he learnt during the Naval Architecture courses at the London School of Engineering and Navigation, he measured up the distances between the stiffeners of the water-tight bulkhead, then mustered a working party of seamen and stokers and put them to work sawing the appropriate lengths of planks and shores. Spanning the stiffeners and knitting them together with thick planks and ramming shores between them and the steam and water drums of the boiler, the working party completed a structure as strong as, if not stronger than, any other water-tight bulkhead in the ship.

Two or three weeks later, a Constructor Commander (a naval architect) complemented the Captain on the professional job made of strengthening the bulkhead. On the recommendations of the Constructor, the young fifth-class shipwright was awarded the BEM (British Empire Medal).

While Ted held no grudge against the young shipwright for being given the award, he did feel let down by the red-tape bureaucracy which had allowed such a miscarriage of appreciation.

With the foremost water-tight bulkhead now strengthened, the *Clinton* could increase her speed ahead. The hydraulic tele-motor system for controlling the steering gear from the bridge had been severed by the explosion and steerage orders were being relayed by word of mouth by seamen stationed at intervals from the bridge along the upper deck and thence through the steering flat hatch to a stoker at the manual control of the steering engine.

Ted's next job was to run lengths of copper pipe to bypass the damaged portion of the steering gear hydraulic control system. Once completed, steering of the *Clinton* reverted back to the wheel-house.

The damaged sweeper made her way into swept waters and slowly steamed to the island of Poros where she anchored.

The flotilla leader had also been mined and had to be towed and beached on the nearby island of Poros. The rest of the flotilla, together with the rest of the invasion force, finally anchored early in the evening in Phaleron Bay and landed their troops and supplies. In all, forty-two mines had been destroyed.

Chapter 31

Ted Meets Spiros

After a week or so the *Clinton* moved into the inner harbour of Piraeus where demolition by the Germans was very severe. The harbour was littered with rusting merchant ships, some listing heavily, others half sunk and others lying on their sides. Large wooden barges, tied up four and five abreast, lined hundreds of feet of the harbour wall. Ted later learnt that it was on these barges that the Germans had loaded every conceivable type of mine and dumped the lot haphazardly into the approaches to Piraeus just prior to the arrival of the British invasion forces.

On the first afternoon after the *Clinton* tied up in Piraeus, Ted went ashore. The place was a scene of utter destruction. The jetty was a mass of shell holes through which the harbour water was visible and rusty wire nets, flattened oil drums and buoys, together with toppled cranes, lay everywhere. Outside the dock area it was sometimes impossible to find the road so he had to climb over the rubble which used to be the houses. Small trees and shrubs were sprouting out of and on the crumbled walls while skinny dogs foraged among the ruins for food and rats.

Eventually the scene of desolation gave way to a wide street which at one time must have been the main avenue with trees lining each side. The occasional tree still stood, but the rest were either shrubs or broken and bent across the road or pavement. The smell of burning pine wood filled the air.

Ted was greeted by most of the friendly inhabitants as he made his way through the dusty sun-lit street. Half-way up the street, he stopped

124

at a taverna. Its doors were wide open and men sat at tables either side of the door playing some sort of game. Ted stepped down and into a dimly lit earthen-floored room. The walls were lined with huge wine casks.

He sat at a table and wondered what to order. A man approached him and in perfect English asked, 'Are you from the damaged sweeper?'

'Yes,' replied Ted.

The man then went on to tell how he had watched the action off Poros from the balcony atop his house with binoculars.

'What you drinking?' he asked.

Ted replied that all the drinks were strange to him and asked what the man suggested.

'Try this,' said the man, pouring a light yellowish drink from a flask into a tin cup. Ted tasted it. It was wine but had a resin taste. He didn't particularly like it at first, but he remembered he'd tasted it previously in Kithera. He went along with the man's choice and ordered a flask. He went to pay and the man said, 'That's on me. That's the least I can do for our British friends.'

The man then introduced himself as Spiros Skouras. He went on to relate how the average Greek next to his own country loved the British and that while the Germans were still in Piraeus, he flew a Union Jack from the top of his house. He told Ted how during the occupation he used to slip out to various resistance meetings and that one night he was returning home after curfew and two German soldiers on patrol, seeing him, ordered him to stop. Spiros, thinking quickly, crouched down and started calling to an imaginary cat, 'Puss, Puss!' The Germans joined in with their 'Puss, Puss!' Eventually, on reaching his front door, he slipped inside quickly whilst the soldiers continued to seek out the 'cat'.

This time Ted insisted on buying a measure of retsina. He put down a piece of paper known as BMA (British Military Administration) money. It had one shilling printed on it. He was given a great wad of Greek paper money. It took him a minute or two to count it. It was over a hundred million drachma. He asked if the owner couldn't give him the change in BMA money. Spiros said the man was sorry but they didn't have any such currency. By the end of the afternoon Ted had spent his hundred million drachma buying drinks for everyone.

After a time he enquired if they had something to eat. He felt a little guilty for he knew that starvation was prevalent throughout Greece. Anyway the taverna owner brought him some hard dry goat's cheese, some coarse bread and a dish full of black and green olives. Spiros then showed him the Greek way to host a guest. It was considered rude to fill a glass to the top, and to show the guest you enjoyed his company you never allowed the glass to become empty. The afternoon gave way to evening and then night. Eventually Spiros invited Ted to his home. The house was large and well built. It stood on the side of a small steep street which ran down to the sea front.

His wife was a dentist and part of the house was occupied by her practice. The trio sat up conversing until the small hours of the morning. The talk was mostly about the German occupation and the harsh life they had endured. Spiros had an intense hatred for the Germans and especially for a particular SS Lieutenant-Colonel who had terrorised the local population and caused the imprisonment and death of many of his neighbours. He went on to relate how one afternoon the SS officer turned up for dental work by his wife. After administering anaesthetic, the Colonel dozed off. Spiros approached him from the back and, sliding the metal breast plate which hung around his neck on a metal chain, he proceeded to rotate the plate such that the chain grew tighter and tighter round his neck. Eventually he choked the officer to death. He then dragged the body down the stairs to his basement where he hacked the body to pieces and threw them into the furnace.

It was dark by then, but he became concerned about the black smoke and the smell belching from the chimney. Next day German troops searched the whole of Piraeus for the missing officer. They searched nearly every house. Spiros, realising his house was one of the next to be visited, did a double check to reassure himself that there was no evidence. He checked everywhere and finally the furnace room. Then he broke out into a hot sweat, for there on the floor was a button from the officer's uniform. He quickly pocketed it just as the search party hammered on the front door.

The late hour and the retsina were taking their toll. Spiros invited Ted to stay the night; he was welcome to sleep on the settee. Ted thanked Spiros and his wife and collapsed on to it. He awoke next morning with the sun pouring through the window into his slit eyes. Dressing hurriedly he knocked on the dining room door. Spiros and his wife were having breakfast. They invited him to sit down and join them. Thanking them, he told them that he was already late and must get aboard immediately. He bade them goodbye and was gone.

He managed to get aboard without being noticed. Popeye had kept his breakfast hot and he slowly went about the routine of the day.

Chapter 32

Patching Up The Sweeper

A South African salvage vessel had recently arrived in Piraeus. There was plenty of work for it, including the *Clinton*. The team of divers, shipwrights and attendants commandeered one of the wooden barges in the harbour and secured it alongside the damaged starboard bow of the sweeper. On the upper deck of the barge they stowed all their diving pumps, generators and tool chests and used the area as their staging level for diving. The lower deck was used for meals and accommodation.

Their first job was to carve out long lengths of twelve by twelve inch timbers which they attached in a vertical plane to whatever was left of the sweeper's original frames. Before attaching them with long steel bolts they had to cut the face of one side of the timber to match the badly distorted contour of the ship's side. This they did by attaching a heavy weight to the end of a long thin plank of wood then lowering the plank vertically into the water with its thin edge touching the ship's side. A diver with a special type of marking pencil gripped between his small finger and the adjacent one would place his outstretched thumb on the ship's side and slowly descend, all the time allowing his thumb to follow the contour of the ship's side, the pencil all the time reproducing the same contour on the plank.

The plank would then be pulled on to the barge where they would use a jigsaw to cut along the pencil line. The plank was then laid onto the twelve by twelve inch timber, where the contour would be transferred. The shipwrights would then set to work with adzes and fashion the timber to match exactly the contour of the ship's side.

In order to ensure a good watertight fit between the vertical timbers and the ship's side, a thick pyramid of white lead would be heaped onto the contoured surface and covered by canvas which was nailed down on both sides of the timber. This would provide a soft joint that would spread out and fill any gap or crevice.

Once the vertical timbers had been secured, horizontal lengths of thick planks were placed butting onto each other from the bottom to the top of the hole in the ship's side. The seams were then caulked, a thick layer of canvas was secured to the entire patch and another layer of thinner planks of wood running in a vertical direction completed the task.

Chapter 33

The Political Scene Ashore

Ted spent a considerable amount of time ashore and especially in Spiros' company. The Germans had pulled out of Athens by now, but the internal political situation in Athens, Piraeus, and for that matter most of the country, was in turmoil and prevented Greece from trying to recover from the Nazi occupation.

As Ted passed one stand in the market selling bread, he watched as a bedraggled old woman opened up a suitcase overflowing with paper money to pay for a loaf of bread. The wind lifted some of the notes and they were carried away down the street. Nobody moved to retrieve them, the old lady least of all, as she continued to hand over the rest of the suitcase's contents. She counted out sixty million drachma in exchange for the bread.

The value of the drachma had practically disappeared. Most shops had put up their shutters as buying and selling had stopped, with consequent hardship, misery and despair. Former rich and middle class Greeks stood in the same queue with the poor, waiting for a bowl of soup. The German occupation had led to a complete breakdown of the social fabric.

Small boys of five and six years of age tugged on Ted's jacket asking for *chocolatto* and gum. They were almost bald, their hair having been cut to prevent lice. They would collect at one end of the inner harbour where the wind had blown all the debris and there they would push their fishing nets under a piece of soggy bread and gently lift it out of the water. Most times the bread would disintegrate. The pieces they did land were generally covered with fuel oil; nevertheless they carefully dried the soggy mass over a fire and when dry, ate it. They even did the same with orange peel.

Other boys that Ted met were a little more frightening and better fed. They were anything from eleven to sixteen years of age; they carried rifles, bandoleers full of cartridges round their shoulders and hand grenades tied round their waists. They were guerillas belonging to ELAS (People's Liberation Front), bands of partisans under Communist rule. Though they smiled and behaved in a friendly manner toward Ted, they left nobody in doubt that one came and went under their authority.

Most free-standing walls in Piraeus had the red hammer and sickle, the letters EAM (for National Liberation Front), KKE (for Greek Communist Party) and ELAS painted on. Spiros was directly opposed to all these groups and was a Royalist. He expressed the opinion many times that these groups were poorly educated and that they didn't really understand the true meaning of Communism and that, as guerrillas, they had fought against the Germans and thought that they were the real rulers of Greece. They wanted nothing to do with the King who had been in exile during the war and they thought they were entitled to take over all the large houses and lands of the rich. Spiros went on to say that he could sit down and talk with these people and within half an hour he could change them from Communist to Royalist.

One day Ted got an invitation from Spiros to attend a party of prominent members of Piraeus society to celebrate the inauguration of the new Mayor. The party was held in the gardens of a wealthy ship-owner's estate. Grape vines laden with fruit draped the white wooden arbours and small white lights twinkled among the leaves. The tables were covered with beautiful golden damask upon which candles flickered in the cool evening breeze and an orchestra was playing in an open space at the far end of the grounds.

As the evening wore on and the guests mellowed, a beautiful woman in a shimmering evening gown started to sing romantic songs. She was known as the Tigress for she usually wore a full-length coat of genuine

131

tiger skin. She asked Ted to sing. He could think of nothing to suit the occasion: his native and rather coarse 'Blaydon Races' was out. He almost started on 'Sorento' but realised how the Greeks hated the Italians; however, the thought of Italians stirred his mind and he sang a song about, 'They can't put it over the Greeks', the 'they' referring to the invasion of Greece by the Italians. The song broke the romantic atmosphere for a while but it soon returned when the Tigress gave forth again.

Ted wondered where all the exotic food and drink came from for ever since he had landed in Greece he'd seen nothing but starvation. At one point the host made a special announcement that in order to honour his guests, the olive oil being used for the meal was from a very special crop from before the war and hidden from the Germans. Ted failed to appreciate what all the fuss was about: olive oil was olive oil. However, the Greeks appeared to be quite excited about the special treat.

Amongst the guests was the British Major in charge of a battalion of Gurkha soldiers assigned to the Piraeus area. Spiros, who was acting as a liaison to the major, introduced him to Ted. It was getting late and as the Major left he shouted across to Ted, 'Don't forget you're invited for Christmas dinner. Spiros will tell you when! Goodnight.'

Athens was out of bounds for the *Clinton*'s crew because of the political situation, but Ted, packing a number of packets of Senior Service into his pockets, headed for the Piraeus railway station and Athens. A mile outside Piraeus the train stopped. After a considerable time, Ted walked up to the driver's cab and through various hand-signs managed to find out the reason for the delay. The driver pointed to an explosive charge protruding from under one of the rails. Ted climbed down and removed it. The same procedure occurred twice more before the train eventually pulled into Athens. It was a beautiful sunny day and people filled the streets. Greek regular army soldiers, armed police and partisans mingled with the crowd.

Ted bartered at a jeweller's for a gold ring which took his fancy. It was an import from Paris. The shop was probably a centre where the Germans had bought gifts for their wives and girlfriends during the occupation.

He then directed his steps toward the Acropolis. It was indeed an impressive sight even though it was a mass of ruins. He marvelled at the skill of the original architects for the way they had designed the steps leading up to the 'High City', for as he placed one foot in front of the other he had the illusion of being lifted up bodily into the complex beyond. Standing on the highest steps of the Parthenon, he had a marvellous view of the whole of Athens below and could trace the railway which he had just arrived on, right back to Piraeus in the distance. It was afternoon now and as he walked down the sunny side of one of the major streets he became aware of people starting to walk in a hurry. Within seconds they were running almost in a panic. Shopkeepers rushed out, pulled down the shutters in front of their windows and then quickly disappeared inside, slamming the doors behind them. Ted found himself standing alone in an absolutely deserted street, then all of a sudden the rat-tat-tat of machine gun bullets filled the air, the bullets causing puffs of sand and dust to burst out of the walls of the buildings.

Ted searched quickly for somewhere to take shelter, when there, across the shaded side of the street, he saw the massive wooden doors of a building slowly closing. He raced across, forced his way through the doors and up a large set of stairs and into a darkened room at the top. He made out the form of a chair in the semi-darkness and sat down huffing and puffing and venting his feelings, and yelled out, 'Bloody Ku Ku E!' (KKE: Communistic Party of Greece). He settled back and, taking a cigarette from one of his packets, lit up. The lighted match revealed he was not alone. His chair was one of a dozen or so and the rest were occupied by a group of solemn-looking men in black suits who were all looking at him. Then he did one great gulp: each of the men had a red hammer and sickle pinned to the lapel of his coat.

He smiled and thought they must have heard his loud 'bloody Ku Ku E!' He immediately pulled out his packet of Senior Service cigarettes and, getting up, offered each a cigarette. Then he went round and offered them a light. The group drew contentedly on their cigarettes and then gave Ted an approving nod.

The men conversed among themselves and Ted listened to find out whether things had returned to normal in the street below. Realising it was getting late and not wanting to make the train journey back to Piraeus in the dark, he decided it was time to leave. He didn't just want to get up and leave without saying anything: it might provoke his communist company. He didn't know the Greek for 'Good afternoon', but he did for 'Goodnight' so with a wave he shouted, *'Kali nichta.'* They waved back, repeating *'Kali nichta,'* and Ted skipped down the stairs, peering out into the street. Everybody was going about their business as usual.

Chapter 34

Civil War

On Sunday 3 December 1944, demonstrations took place in Constiˈution Square, Athens, which led to a clash between the crowd and the police. The police fired a machine gun into the civilian crowd, killing a number of people. Among the so-called civilians were many full-armed ELAS guerillas. Thus began the Greek civil war. Actually the war had been caused by the communist leaders, and the majority of rebels with all their genuine patriotism had become the instrument of communist ambition.

Just over a week before Christmas, Spiros informed Ted that the Major had decided to move the Christmas dinner to the next day because he expected rebel activity in and around Piraeus to increase about Christmas Day.

Next day Ted duly arrived at a building in the centre of Piraeus which had been the German Headquarters. A long table was set up in the centre of a barrack-like room. The room was decorated with all sorts of coloured paper and a few balloons. The Major's men had obviously scraped around for any decorative material in order to create a festive atmosphere. The tablecloth comprised British and Greek flags on which palm branches had been laid. Along the centre of the table were bowls of oranges, figs, peaches and olives.

The Major sat at the head of the table and his assistant, a Captain, occupied the seat at the other end. On either side sat approximately ten persons made up of junior officers, a Greek priest and some city officials. Ted sat with Spiros half-way up the table.

The Major asked everyone to fill their glass with the red wine. He then called for a toast to the Greek Government, followed by a toast to His Majesty King George. Army privates served up lamb and various vegetables. The assembly was by now getting into the spirit of the season. Just prior to dessert being served, the lights flickered, went out, and came back on again. Then the sound of small arms fire could be heard. The Major had obviously heard as he summoned a Sergeant and whispered something into his ear. The festive mood continued, then suddenly the lights went out followed by a terrific explosion as the roof fell in. Cement and other rubble completely covered the table by which time most of the guests, smothered in grey dust, were lying flat under the table. Part of the devastation became visible as guests lit matches and cigarette lighters. Then the Major's voice could be heard, announcing, 'Sorry gentlemen, but we've just been hit by a rebel mortar.' Then he went on to shout, 'Lieutenant Howe, you take Ted back to his ship!'

Ted shouted back, 'Thank you, Sir!'

'That's all right, we'll resume our Christmas dinner at some other time,' replied the Major.

Lieutenant Howe directed Ted to get into an armoured troop carrier. Since no roads existed in the area, having been completely covered in mountains of brick, stone and other rubble, the caterpillar tracks of the troop carrier just climbed up the mountain of debris and down the other side. The lieutenant knew where Ted's ship lay and steered exactly as the crow flies over anything that lay in his path. Ted arrived back at the *Clinton* in a matter of five minutes after leaving the ravage-torn scene of the party.

The civil war heated up in the port area of Piraeus and the *Clinton* was ordered to leave and seek a safe anchorage in Salamis Bay.

During the following days, Ted watched the battle for Athens from the upper deck of the sweeper. It was bitterly cold and snow covered the mountains on the northern outskirts of Athens. Ted could see the red and golden streaks of tracer bullets from the machine guns of the Royal Air Force's Beaufighters ripping into the rebel positions and the occasional flash as bombs exploded.

While working on a piece of machinery in the engine room, Ted received a rather painful and damaging injury to his thumb. He was concerned that some bones might have been fractured or even broken. Next morning he decided to visit a doctor aboard the British hospital ship, *Maine*, which was lying at anchor a few miles from the *Clinton*.

To get to the *Maine* he had to catch a transport from Piraeus. The transport was an infantry landing craft. Ted climbed aboard. He was standing just outside the wheel house and as he looked down into the well of the craft he saw line after line of stretchers, each occupied by a Gurkha soldier. There must have been well over one hundred. Each had severe wounds, some with half their face missing, others with mangled legs, some with terrible stomach wounds and yet others with arms almost severed from their bodies. As Ted looked down at this mass of bleeding and pain-ridden humanity he wondered what he was doing here with his puny injury. He felt like turning back but the transport was already on its way. These soldiers were surely some of the bravest in the world, for not once during the long and choppy trip out to the *Maine* did one of them make a sound, not even a moan or groan.

Once aboard the *Maine*, Ted was directed to a waiting room. As he sat there he could see the doctors working feverishly in blood-soaked white coats. After some time a doctor flung open the door wide and said to Ted, 'Chief, come here, I want you to stand by this steriliser and open it for me every time I come over for a sterilised wadding.'

Ted stood there all afternoon and into the evening as the doctor packed the wadding into the cavities of the Gurkhas' heads, chests and abdomens. Every now and again the doctor would throw up his hands as another soldier died on the operating table. Calling the sickbay attendants, the doctor would direct them to wheel the latest fatality off to the morgue. In a somewhat gruesome but basically practical way, the Chief sickbay attendant would make a comment about each death making available another spare bed.

In the late evening the doctor was relieved and so was Ted. Ted made his way back to the *Clinton*. He never did get his smashed thumb fixed.

He thought how the Major must be missing all these Gurkha soldiers;

they were part of his battalion. Ted also thought about what the Major had once told him about the worst punishment one could inflict on a Gurkha: it was to keep him in barracks, peeling potatoes. They were happiest when they were in action.

A few days later it was deemed safe enough for the *Clinton* to re-enter the harbour of Piraeus and for the South African salvage divers to carry on completing the wooden patch over the hole in her starboard bow. That first afternoon Ted went ashore and met Spiros in his favourite taverna. The streets were in an even worse condition than before. Spiros spoke of the number of innocent civilians that had been massacred by the Communist rebels and as Ted and he returned to his home he pointed to the bodies of dozens of Bulgarian, Romanian and Albanian prostitutes who had had their throats cut by the rebels because of fraternising with the Germans. Spiros also went on to explain his brush with death. The rebels began to realise he was assisting the British forces under the Major and early one morning kidnapped him outside his house, pushed him into the side car of a motorbike and sped away with him. Luckily some of the Major's men saw the incident happen and gave chase in a jeep. Once they were adjacent to the motorbike and side car they shot the rebel driving the motorbike. The bike and sidecar with Spiros turned over. He was pulled out with only a few bumps and bruises.

A few days later Ted bumped into the Major marching two dozen of his Gurkhas down the street. Spiros was also in his company. Apparently there was a high building in the centre of Piraeus that had been taken over by the rebels. General Scobie, the British officer in charge of operations in Greece, had called for all rebels to hand in their arms by a certain date and time. The Major was about to see these orders complied with by the rebels in the high building.

Lining up his men outside the building and using a loudspeaker, he called for the communists inside to come out with their hands up in the air and lay down their arms in front of the Major. After a few minutes, nothing appeared to be happening. Spiros approached the Major and suggested he go in and speak to them. The Major wouldn't hear of it. Eventually Spiros convinced the Major that he knew the mentality of the people and that they would listen to him.

The Major said, 'All right, I'll give you four minutes. If nothing happens I'll blow the building to smithereens!'

Spiros limped in and after what seemed like ages, the rebels started slowly to move out with hands above their heads and dropped their fire-arms at the feet of the Major.

Spiros was the last to emerge. It had taken three minutes.

Chapter 35

Churchill Arrives

It was Christmas day 1944. Mr Winston Churchill and Mr Anthony Eden had flown out from England to try to negotiate an end to the Greek Civil War.

A bitterly cold wind was blowing in from the mountains as the two politicians boarded HMS *Ajax*, now lying with her stern tied at right-angles to the jetty, whilst both of her bow anchors were streamed out into the middle of the harbour. Ted's sweeper was tied up across the jetty directly opposite the *Ajax*. That evening, Ted went aboard the *Ajax* to meet some of his fellow classmates serving aboard the cruiser.

During this time Archbishop Damaskinos arrived from Athens to hold a conference with Mr Churchill. The Archbishop was a splendid figure well over six feet tall in black robes with a black hood draped over his orthodox hat and carrying a long black ebony cane with a silver top. Since it was Christmas, the *Ajax*'s sailors had dressed up in every kind of costume and disguise: as Chinese, Negroes, Red Indians, Cockneys and clowns. The Archbishop, in his robes and high hat, and the sailors met. The sailors thought he was part of their show. Some of them even pulled his beard to find out whether it was true or false as the rest danced around him enthusiastically. The Archbishop thought this motley gang was a premeditated insult and made strides to return to Athens. Fortunately the Captain came upon the scene of the sailors dancing round the Archbishop and rescued him. After spending some time trying to explain the embarrassing situation to the Archbishop, the cleric eventually simmered down and was led off to meet Mr Churchill.

The following afternoon, Boxing Day, as Ted leaned over the *Clinton*'s upper deck rail, he saw Mr Churchill, Mr Eden and the British Admiral coming ashore from the *Ajax*. As Mr Churchill passed Ted he stopped and, looking at the *Clinton*, asked, 'What happened?' Ted explained. Mr Churchill then stepped forward, thrusting his hand upwards to shake Ted's hand. Ted in the meantime held up his grease-laden hands indicating how dirty they were. Churchill took no notice and shook his hand none the less. With that he yelled, 'Well done!', gave his familiar 'V for Victory' sign and strode off.

During the whole episode the Greek Admiral had joined Mr Churchill's party from his flagship, the *Averoff*. All the time rebels were spraying the area with small arms fire and occasionally lobbing mortars. Ted stood with his back to the *Clinton*'s funnel, using it as a shield. In the meantime Mr Churchill with his chin stuck forward strode defiantly along the dock side as bullets ricocheted amongst the hardware along the quay. The little Greek Admiral was trailing well behind as he darted in and out from behind oil drums and other barricades. Mr Churchill reached his armoured car and waited for the remainder of his party. Then, with a military escort, they were off to the British Embassy in Athens.

As the armoured car pulled away, Ted thought about this seventy-year-old man and how fortunate his country was to have such an indomitable leader at this time in its history. He had left the festive and comfortable atmosphere of his home on Christmas Eve at grave personal risk to his health and his life. He was also being severely criticised by the British and American press, together with many Members of Parliament for his Greek policies. On top of this, problems in Poland and the Battle of the Bulge were occupying his mind. However he realised that the Greek situation had the potential of getting out of hand and that if the rebels succeeded the whole of Greece would fall under Soviet domination.

But the more immediate concern of Churchill's was that troops essential to the total liberation of Italy were being diverted to the Greek trouble spot. Eventually Churchill's policy paid off. The majority of Greeks accepted his solution to the problem and finally elected Archbishop

Damaskinos as Regent.

The Battle of Athens had lasted five weeks and on 3 January a truce was signed and peace returned.

On 6 January 1945, Ted's first daughter Patricia Anne was born, way back in England.

On 12 February, Mr Churchill was persuaded to call in at Athens on his way back from the Yalta Conference. He accepted and was given the most overwhelming reception that any non-Greek had received in the ancient city. Eventually the British press and Parliament, together with the Americans, were forced to admit that the old man's policies had been correct.

Chapter 36

The Third Tiffy and Sweeper Part

The *Clinton*'s patch was complete by now and the flooded forward end had been pumped dry. As Ted entered the seamen's lower mess, the stench was overpowering. He found the hammock bin was now occupied by great sides of rotting meat which had floated up from the provision rooms and the soggy hammocks had sunk down into the area where the meat had originally been stored. He examined the shipboard side of the patch and found it to be watertight. As a precaution the suction hoses of the salvage pump located on the fo'c'sle remained in place in case of water seeping through the patch.

It was time for the *Clinton* to leave Piraeus for a permanent repair job to her holed hull. Ted went ashore to say goodbye to Spiros. He gave him a few packets of Senior Service cigarettes and then Spiros opened the door to his safe and pulled out a whole pile of envelopes tied up with string. He explained that they were letters addressed to British soldiers of the Royal Northumberland Fusiliers which had been left behind when the British were driven out by the Germans in 1941.

Spiros went on to explain that the Germans had flung the letters on the road and trampled on them to show their contempt as they marched triumphant through Piraeus. After the Germans had passed by, Spiros collected as many of the letters as possible and now he handed them over to Ted and requested that he return them to his fellow countrymen. Among the letters were some from his home town of Alnwick.

The next morning the *Clinton* sailed for Taranto, Italy. A day out from

Taranto, the sweeper ran into some heavy weather and Ted grew concerned about the constant pounding to which the wooden patch was being subjected. He kept checking to ensure the salvage pumps were in good working condition.

During one particularly bad period when the sweeper was burying her nose deep into the head seas, Ted heard and felt a dull thud up forward. Taking his flashlight and staggering into the compartment, one side of which was formed by the patch, he observed that the electric generator's spare rotor had become displaced from its stowage location up high near the deck-head and had plummeted down and that its four-inch steel shaft had punched a hole through the patch. Luckily the shaft appeared to be acting like a well-fitting plug as the soggy wood swelled up around it and so the rotor was left until the vessel was dry-docked.

As Ted left the compartment, he thought, what a stupid location to stow a piece of electrical equipment.

The sweeper slowly made her way across the vast expanse of Taranto's inner harbour. Three or four Italian battleships together with some destroyers and smaller vessels, all badly damaged, lay scattered across the tranquil anchorage.

The *Clinton* nosed into a floating dry-dock at the extreme northern end of the harbour. After two hours the dock had raised her high and dry and within another few hours the Italian shipyard workers had removed the wooden patch. At last Ted saw the damage the mine had inflicted. The area of torn, jagged and twisted steel was enormous, big enough to accommodate a double-decker bus.

It had come time for Ted and the sweeper to part. The ship's company was reduced to the very minimum for the repair period.

Ted embarked on an Italian cruiser for Malta, where he joined a Hunt-class destroyer and ended the war off the Yugoslavian coast. His destroyer then tried to prevent the take-over of Trieste by the Yugoslavian army, but that's another story.

The *Clinton* rejoined the 5th Minesweeping Flotilla in September 1945 and continued to sweep the seas round Greece, Malta, North Africa and Albania. In January 1947 she was returned to the United States Navy.

She had been part of the 'Lease-lend' programme and in November 1947 the sweeper was sold and scrapped. Her original Captain, Lieutenant-Commander K.A. Gadd, DSC, became a Commodore and a Commander of the British Empire. In 1996 Ted's daughter Patricia Anne (a Toronto lawyer), became a Freeman of the City of London.

'IN SWEEPS!'